gill & macmillan primary

What is the main focus of *Sounds Good Phonics 3*?
The main focus is to teach English spelling in a clear, systematic manner. English is a tricky language with a wide variety of ways in which a sound may be spelt. For example the sound **/ee/** may be spelt using the letters **ee** as in **sheep**, **ea** as in **cheap** or with **y** at the end of a word as in **holly**. Many of us learnt to spell by mentally taking note of how various words were spelt when we were reading. However, most pupils need a systematic approach. *Sounds Good Phonics* offers this structure, going through a range of sounds and introducing the variety of ways they may be spelt.

What sounds are covered in *Sounds Good Phonics 3*?
To view the sounds covered in *Sounds Good Phonics 3* refer to the contents page overleaf or the reference grid at the back of the activity book.

How do I navigate this activity book?
The activity book is easy to navigate and a table of contents is supplied.

Here details the sound.

Here details the variations of spelling the sound.

Revision of all spellings of the sound.

/ee/ sound	
/ee/ sound spelt with the letters **ee**	64
/ee/ sound spelt with the letter **y (as in holly)**	65
/ee/ sound spelt with the letters **ea**	66
/ee/ sound spelt with the letters **ee**, **y (as in holly)**, **ea**	67

Do I need to follow this activity book page by page in sequence?
This activity book is not designed to be used in that manner. If you look at the contents page overleaf you will see that the first half of the book is presented in a most sequential manner, focusing on revision, double consonants, initial blends, final blends and Magic E. It is best to cover this first part of the book initially.

The second half of the book focuses on the sounds **/ee/**, **/ai/**, **/ie/**, **/oa/**, **/ue/**, **/oi/**, **/ou/**, **/or/** and **/er/**. These sounds may be dipped in and out of as you please. For example, as previously mentioned the sound **/ee/** may be spelt with the variations **ee**, **ea** and **y** at the end of a word. Most teachers prefer not to teach these all at once as it will generally cause confusion. Instead it is best to introduce the **ee** spelling of **/ee/**, perhaps teach another sound and only progress to the next variation of spelling **/ee/**, for example **ea**, when pupils have fully grasped the initial **ee** spelling of **/ee/**.

I am unsure of the variety of spellings for each sound, for example the variety of ways to spell /ee/.

A chart detailing alternative spellings for each sound is available both inside the back cover of this activity book and in the teacher's handbook. The chart at the back of the activity book acts as a good reference guide for parents when doing homework.

A design feature which also addresses this involves the little characters you encounter at the top of some pages.

The speech bubble indicates what sound they make and the letters printed on each of their bodies indicate the variety of ways in which the sound may be spelt.

Are any of the sounds in *Sounds Good Phonics 3*, such as /ee/, /ai/, or /oi/, presented in *Sounds Good Phonics 1* and *Sounds Good Phonics 2*?

No, these sounds are not covered in the first two activity books, as research indicated that some schools cover them at this level, but others do not. However, age-related worksheets are available on the accompanying website, www.phonics.ie. You may like to print and photocopy these worksheets to introduce the sounds, if your pupils have not been formally taught them previously.

I see you use the symbols //, what do these refer to?

To avoid confusion between sounds and letters, *Sounds Good Phonics* uses the symbols // to indicate a sound. For example, the letters **ay** in the word ray make the sound **/ai/**.

Contents

Revision

Revision: Initial consonant sounds 6
Revision: Initial vowel sounds 8
Revision: Medial vowel sounds 9
Revision: Blending 10

Blends

Blend **ch** 13
Blend **sh** 14
Blend **qu** 15
Blend **th** 16
Blend **wh** 17
Revision: **ch**, **sh**, **qu**, **th**, **wh** 18

Double consonants

Double consonant **ll** 20
Double consonant **ff** 21
Double consonant **ss**, **zz** 22
Revision: **ll**, **ff**, **ss**, **zz** 23

Initial blends

Initial blends **bl**, **br**, **cl**, **cr** 24
Initial blends **dr**, **tr**, **fl**, **fr** 26
Initial blends **gl**, **gr**, **pl**, **pr** 28
Initial blends **sc**, **sk**, **sm**, **sn** 30
Initial blends **sl**, **sp**, **st**, **sw** 32
Revision: **bl**, **br**, **cl**, **cr**, **dr**, **tr**, **fl**, **fr**, **gl**, **gr**, **pl**, **pr**, **sc**, **sk**, **sm**, **sn**, **sl**, **sp**, **st**, **sw** 34

Final blends

Final blends **lt**, **mp** 37
Final blends **nd**, **nt** 38
Final blends **sp**, **st** 39
Revision: **lt**, **mp**, **nd**, **nt**, **sp**, **st** 40
/c/ sound spelt with the letters **ck** 41
/ng/ sound spelt with the letters **ng** 43
/ng//k/ sound spelt with the letters **nk** 45

Magic E

Magic E with **a** 47
Magic E with **i** 50
Magic E with **o** 53
Magic E with **u** 56
Magic E with initial blends 59

/ee/ sound

/ee/ sound spelt with the letters **ee** 64
/ee/ sound spelt with the letter **y (as in holly)** 65
/ee/ sound spelt with the letters **ea** 66
/ee/ sound spelt with the letters **ee**, **y (as in holly)**, **ea** 67

/ai/ sound

/ai/ sound spelt with the letters **ai** 70
/ai/ sound spelt with the letters **ay** 71
/ai/ sound spelt with the letters **ai**, **Magic E** with **a**, **ay** 72

/ie/ sound

/ie/ sound spelt with the letters **ie** 75
/ie/ sound spelt with the letter **y (as in fly)** 76
/ie/ sound spelt with the letters **igh** 77
/ie/ sound spelt with the letters **ie**, **Magic E** with **i**, **y (as in holly)**, **igh** 78

/oa/ sound

/oa/ sound spelt with the letters **oa** 81
/oa/ sound spelt with the letters **ow** 82
/oa/ sound spelt with the letters **oa**, **Magic E** with **o**, **ow** 83

/ue/ sound

/ue/ sound spelt with the letters **ue** 86
/ue/ sound spelt with the letters **ew** 87
/ue/ sound spelt with the letters **oa**, **Magic E** with **o**, **ew** 88

/oi/ sound

/oi/ sound spelt with the letters **oi** 91
/oi/ sound spelt with the letters **oy** 92
/oi/ sound spelt with the letters **oi**, **oy** 93

/ou/ sound

/ou/ sound spelt with the letters **ou** 96
/ou/ sound spelt with the letters **ow** 97
/ou/ sound spelt with the letters **ou**, **ow** 98

/or/ and /aw/ sounds

/or/ sound spelt with the letters **or** 101
/aw/ sound spelt with the letters **al** 102
/aw/ sound spelt with the letters **au** 103
/aw/ sound spelt with the letters **aw** 104
/aw/ sound spelt with the letters **or**, **al**, **au**, **aw** 105

/ur/ sound

/ur/ sound spelt with the letters **er** 106
/ur/ sound spelt with the letters **ir** 107
/ur/ sound spelt with the letters **ur** 108
/ur/ sound spelt with the letters **er**, **ir**, **ur** 109

Say each word. Colour the sound you hear at the beginning and end of the word.

Objective: The child will be enabled to identify the 26 sounds of the alphabet and identify initial and final sounds.

Say each word. Write the sound you hear at the beginning and end of the word.

Objective: The child will be enabled to identify the 26 sounds of the alphabet and identify initial and final sounds.

Circle and colour all the vowels.

a
e
i
o
u

a f o s l u e o a e i c i

Say each word. Write the vowel you hear at the beginning of the word.

Objective: The child will be enabled to identify the vowels **a**, **e**, **i**, **o**, **u** and identify items with the initial vowel sounds.

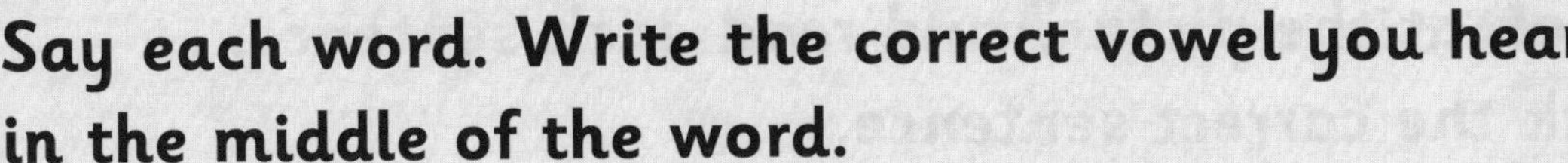

Say each word. Write the correct vowel you hear in the middle of the word.

c__r

c__p

w_g

n__t

h__t

n__t

c__t

c__t

p__n

b__d

p__g

d__g

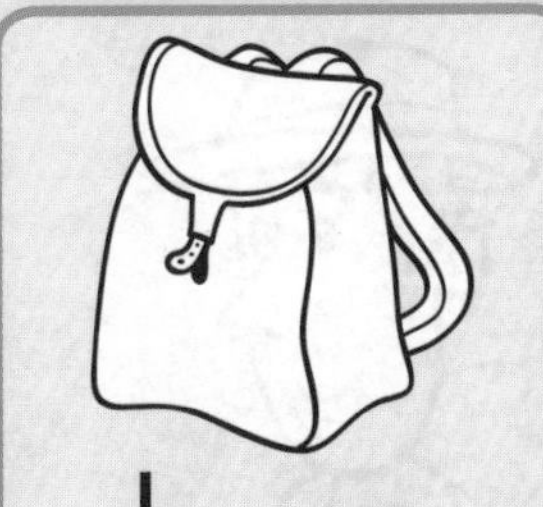

b__g

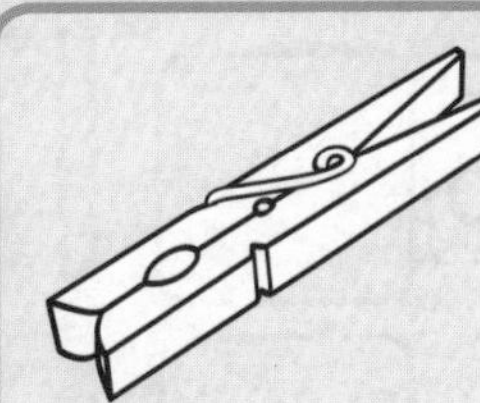

p__g

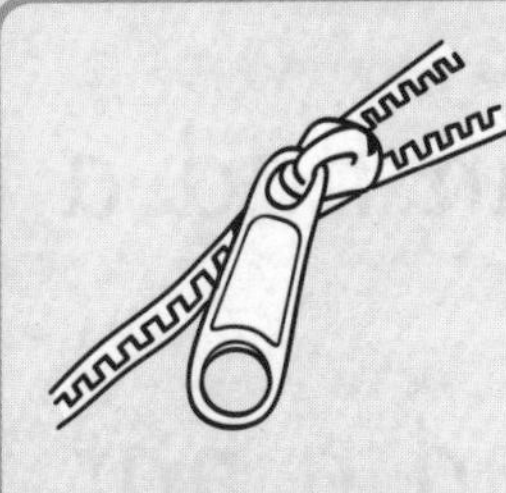

z__p

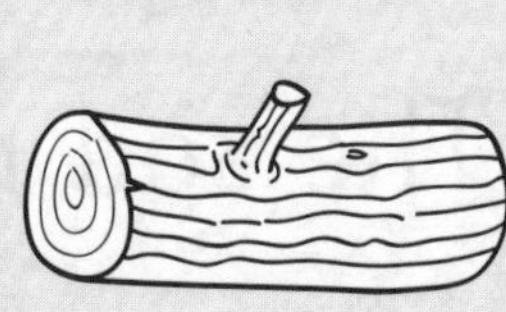

l__g

j__t

g__n

b__n

f__x

Objective: The child will be enabled to identify and supply medial vowel sounds.

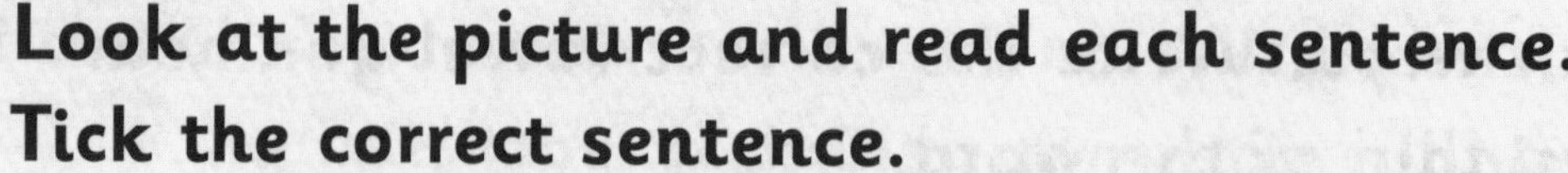

Look at the picture and read each sentence.
Tick the correct sentence.

The pig is in the pen. ☐

The pig sat in the mud. ☐

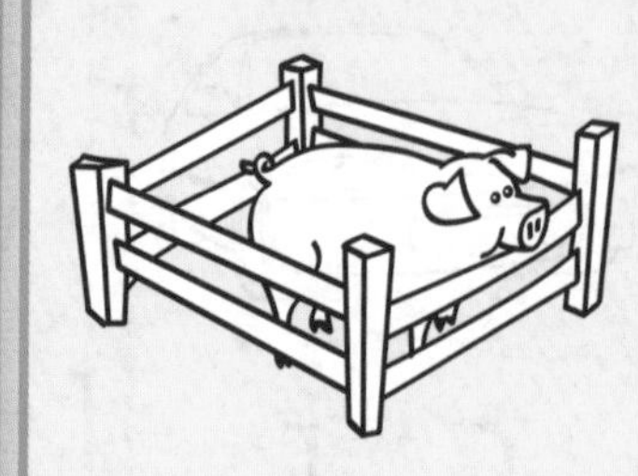

Get the cot and the bib. ☐

The bib is in the cot. ☐

The cat hid in the bin. ☐

The cat is on the bin. ☐

The sad man had a cap. ☐

The man had a hat. ☐

The big man ran. ☐

The big man had a nap. ☐

Objective: The child will be enabled to read simple sentences with CVC words.

Look at the picture and read the sentence. Cross out the word that does not belong in each sentence.

Dad can fix the ~~cat~~ van.

The vet put sat the fox in a big box.

The big, fat cat jet sat on the mat.

The man pen had a bun with jam on top.

The cat and the mop dog ran into the hut.

The man put dot the lid on the bin.

The fat pig ran jar in the mud.

Dad did not red rub the mad dog.

Objective: The child will be enabled to read simple sentences with CVC words and identify which word does not belong in a sentence.

Look at the picture and read the sentence. Cross out the word that does not belong in each sentence.

Tom put ten red ~~cats~~ pens in the bin.

The red nap hen is in the hut.

The big, fat cat had a nap wet in the sun.

Six men wig got on the big, red bus.

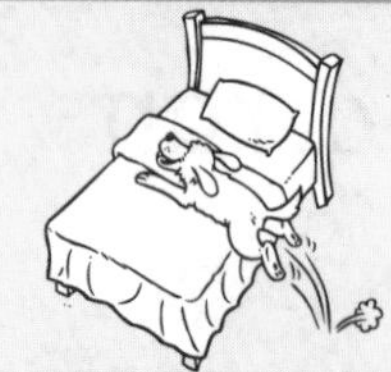

Do not let the bib dog hop on the bed.

It was too hot so Tom got bad the fan.

Put the box and the bag sad in the hut.

Dan put a zip big hat on the cat.

Objective: The child will be enabled to read simple sentences with CVC words and identify which word does not belong in a sentence.

Say each word. Where do you hear the ch sound – the beginning, middle or the end of the word? Write the ch sound in the correct box.

Read the words and write the correct word under each picture.

chips
chin
chop
patch
match
punch

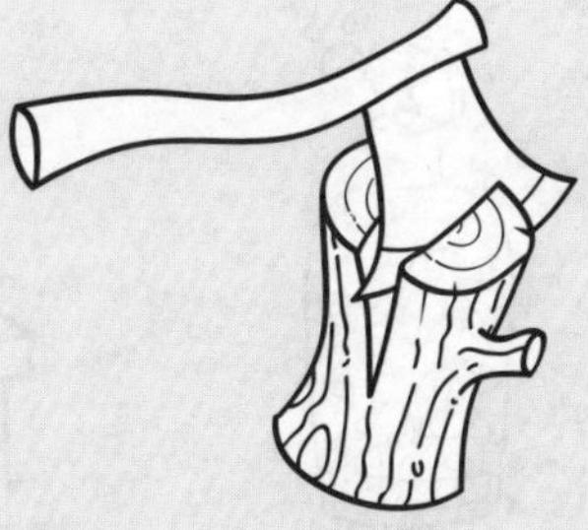

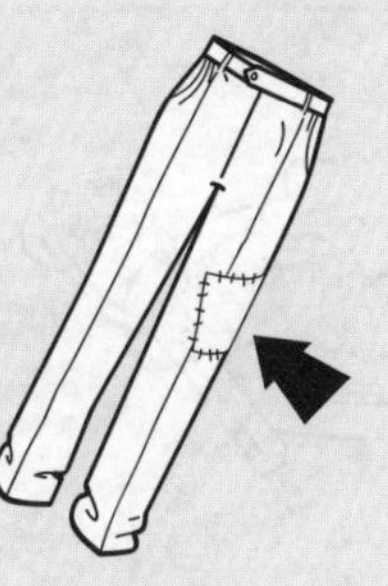

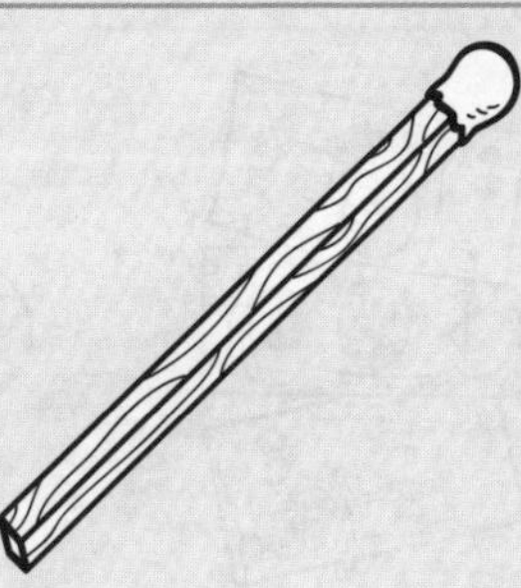

Objective: The child will be enabled to identify if the **/ch/** sound is an initial, final or medial sound in a word, and to read and match simple words with the **/ch/** sound.

Say each word. Where do you hear the sh sound – the beginning, middle or the end of the word? Write the sh sound in the correct box.

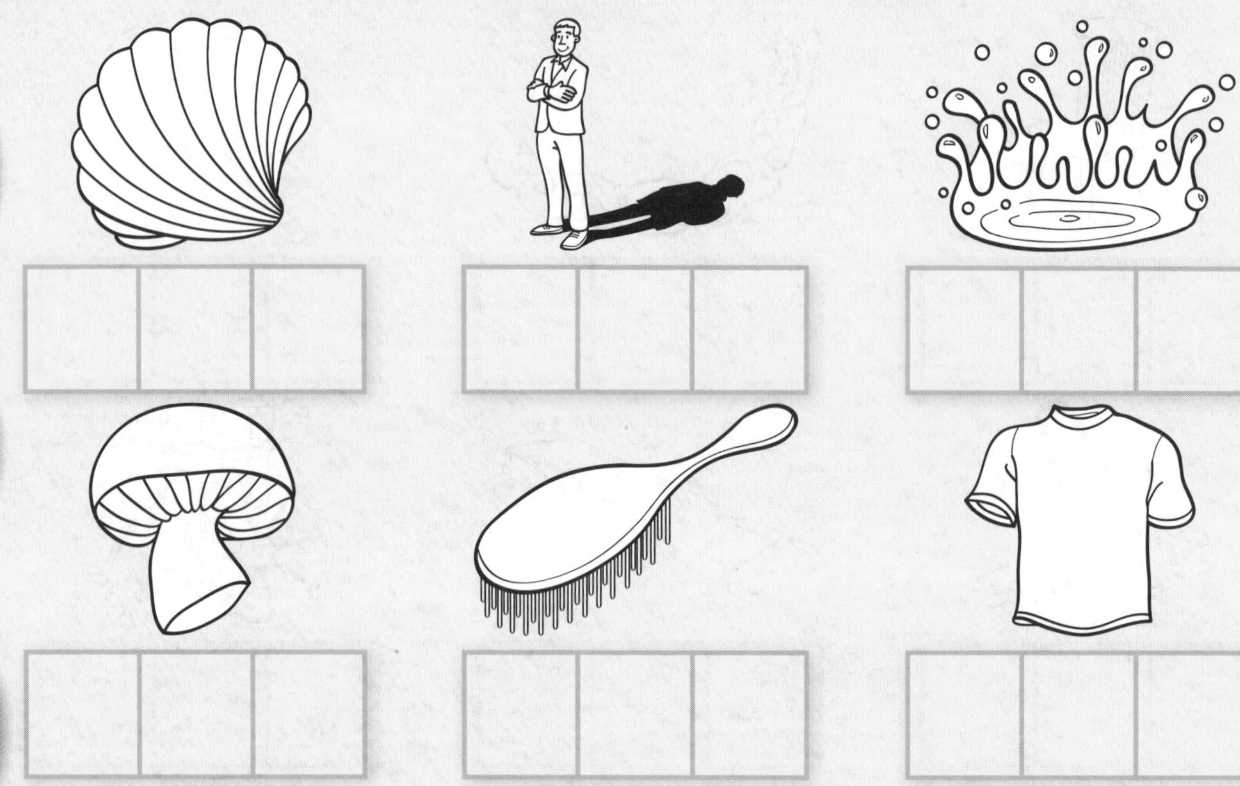

Read the words and write the correct word under each picture.

shelf

shop

mash

cash

polish

shampoo

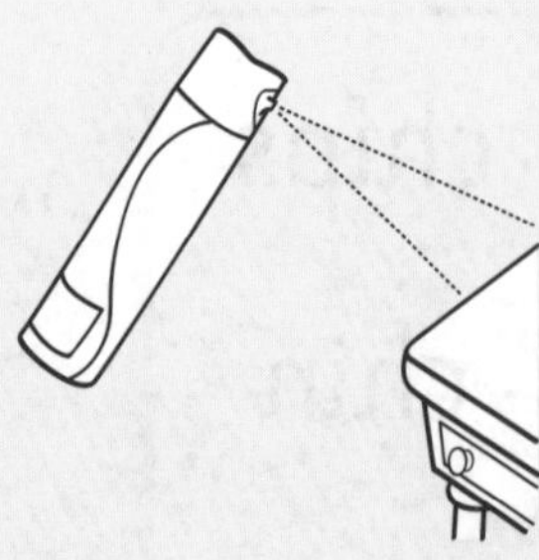

Objective: The child will be enabled to identify if the **/sh/** sound is an initial, final or medial sound in a word, and to read and match simple words with the **/sh/** sound.

Say each word. Where do you hear the qu sound – the beginning, middle or the end of the word? Write the qu sound in the correct box.

Read the words and write the correct word under each picture.

quilt
queen
quad
quiz

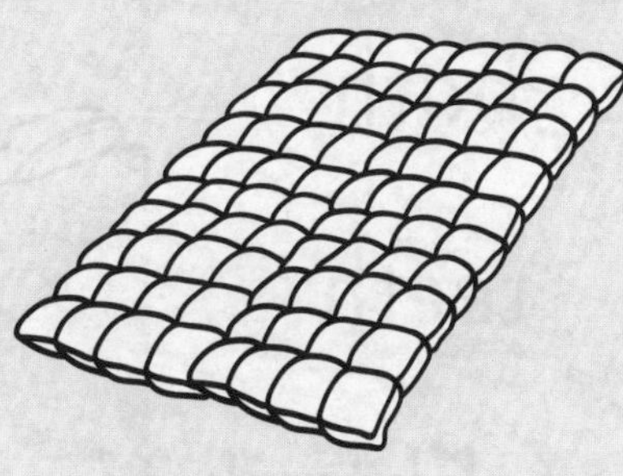

Objective: The child will be enabled to identify if the **/qu/** sound is an initial or medial sound in a word, and to read and match simple words with the **/qu/** sound.

Say each word. Where do you hear the th sound – the beginning, middle or the end of the word? Write the th sound in the correct box.

Read the words and write the correct word under each picture.

moth

path

three

bath

teeth

toothbrush

Objective: The child will be enabled to identify if the **/th/** sound is an initial, final or medial sound in a word, and to read and match simple words with the **/th/** sound.

Say each word. Do you hear the wh sound in the word? Colour the picture. Write the wh sound in the correct box.

Read the words and write the correct word under each picture.

whip

what

wheel

wham

when

whiz

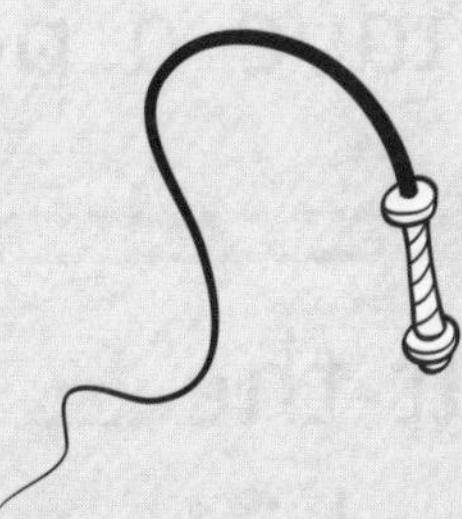

Objective: The child will be enabled to identify words with the initial **/wh/** sound, and to read and match simple words with the **/wh/** sound.

Read the sentences and fill in the correct word.

quad quilt	I put a ________ on the bed. 
whip when	That man has a ________.
shed shut	Will you put the dog in the ________?
bath path	I had a hot ________. 
fish dish	I have a pet ________.
rubbish mash	Put the ________ in the bin. 
chaps chips	I had a bag of ________ for my lunch.
chum chat	I had a big ________ with Dad. 

Objective: The child will be enabled to complete cloze procedure activities based on vocabulary with the blends **ch**, **sh**, **qu**, **th** and **wh**.

Read the sentences and fill in the correct word.

chap chin	The bat hit me on the ________.
shop ship	I got lots of sweets in the ________.
fish dish	I got a ________ in the pet shop.
mash cash	That posh man has lots of ________.
cash rash	I got a red ________ on my leg.
gash mash	I fell and got a ________ on my chin.
church bench	The thin man sat on the ________.
match watch	Can I ________ TV?

Objective: The child will be enabled to complete cloze procedure activities based on vocabulary with the blends **ch**, **sh**, **qu**, **th** and **wh**.

Say each word. Where do you hear the ll sound – the middle or the end of the word? Write the ll sound in the correct box.

Read the words and write the correct word under each picture.

hill
bell
fell
shell
doll
quill

Objective: The child will be enabled to identify if the /ll/ sound is a final or medial sound in a word, and to read and match simple words with the final /ll/ sound.

Say each word. Where do you hear the ff sound – the middle or the end of the word? Write the ff sound in the correct box.

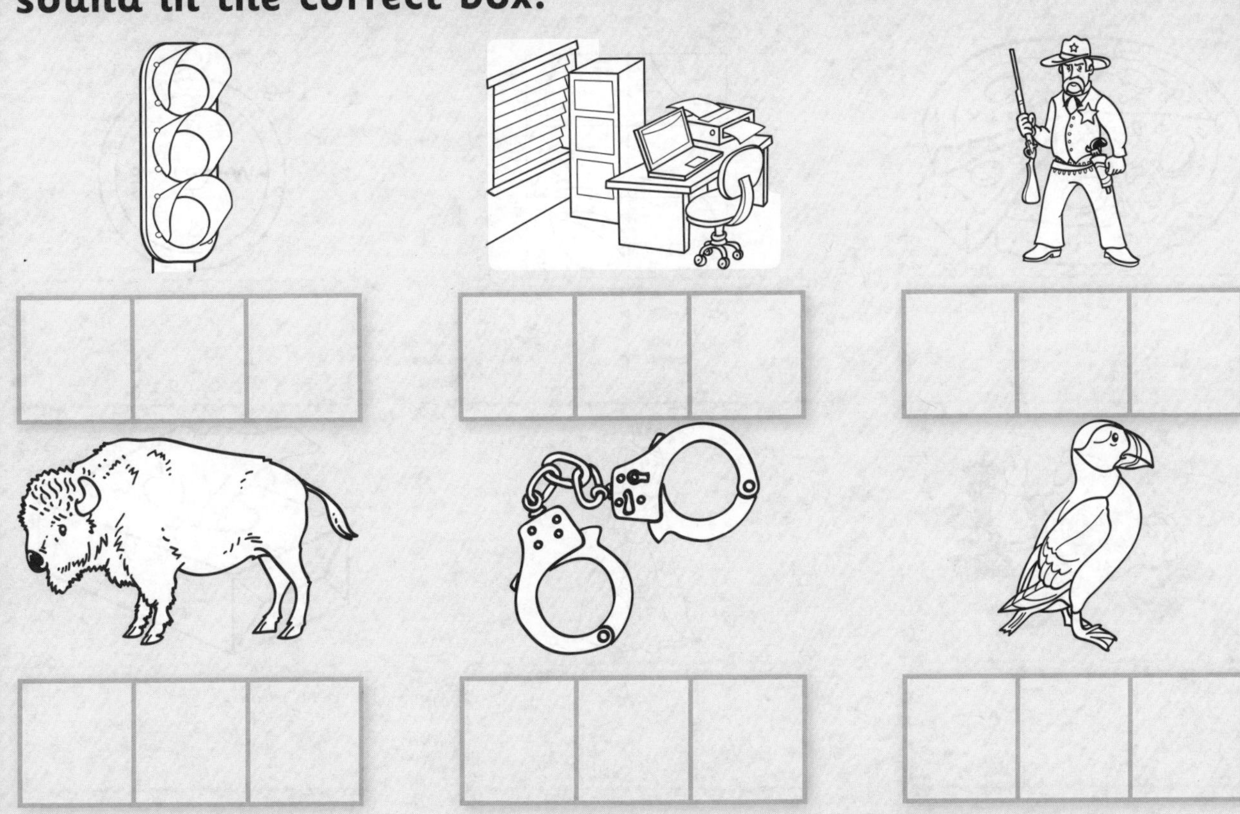

Read the words and write the correct word under each picture.

off
puff
cuff
whiff

Objective: The child will be enabled to identify if the **/ff/** sound is a final or medial sound in a word, and to read and match simple words with the final **/ff/** sound.

Double consonant ss,zz

Say each word. Where do you hear the ss or zz sound – the middle or the end of the word? Write the ss or zz sound in the correct box.

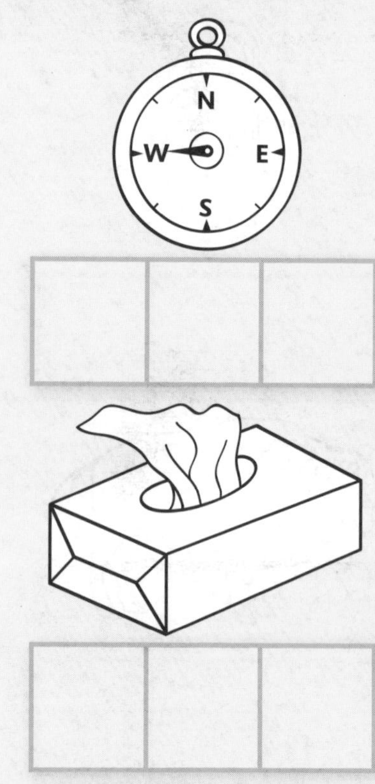

Read the words and write the correct word under each picture.

chess

mess

toss

fizz

kiss

hiss

Objective: The child will be enabled to identify if the **/ss/** and **/zz/** sounds are final or medial sounds in words, and to read and match simple words with the final **/ss/** and **/zz/** sounds.

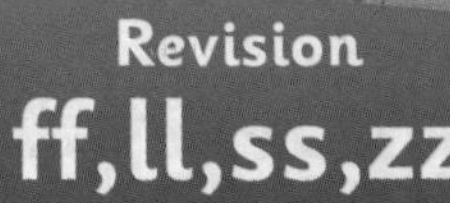

Read the sentences and fill in the correct word.

well yell	Do not ____________ at me. 
well will	Tell Dad we ____________ have lunch at three.
fill fell	The cat ____________ off the wall. 
puss pass	Will you ____________ me the ball?
well will	When I was ill I was not ____________.
doll bull	I gave my ____________ a big kiss. 
coffin coffee	I had a cup of hot ____________.
hiss kiss	Gran likes to give me a big ____________. 

Objective: The child will be enabled to complete cloze procedure activities based on vocabulary with the double consonants **ff, ll, ss** and **zz**.

Say each word. Do you hear the bl, br, cl or cr sound at the beginning of the word? Write the sound you hear.

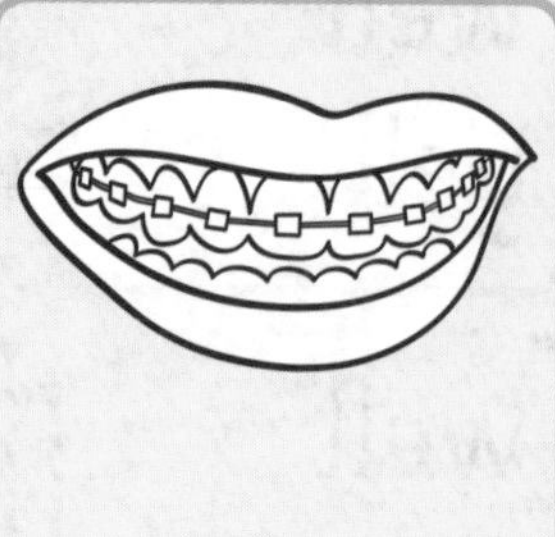

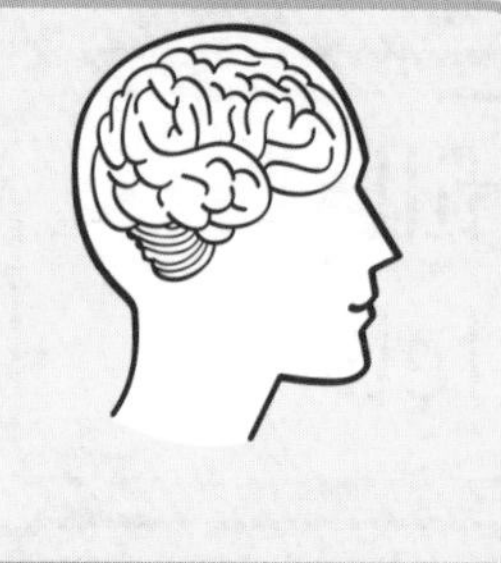

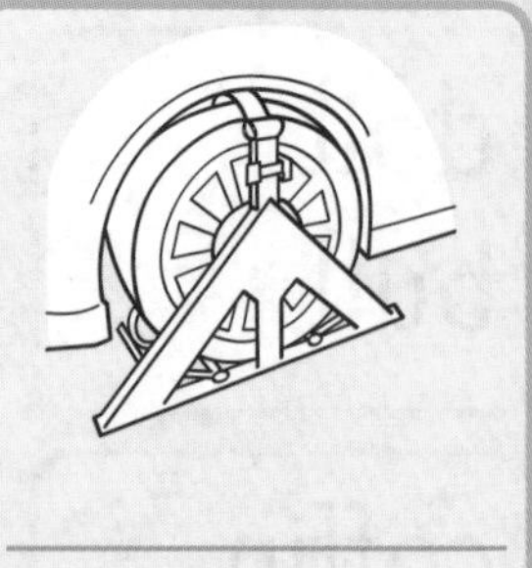

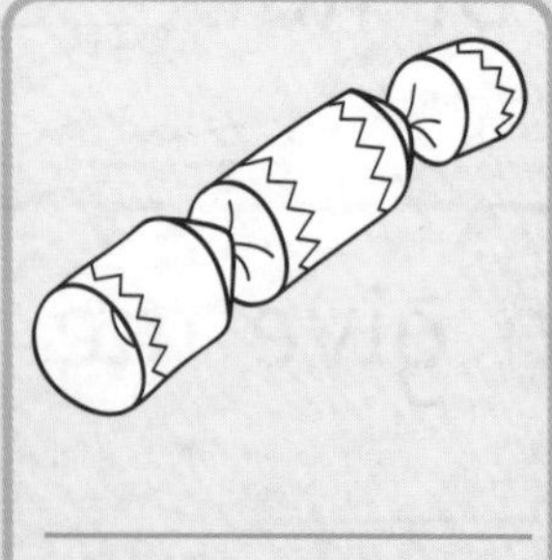

Objective: The child will be enabled to identify items with the initial blends **bl**, **br**, **cl** and **cr**.

Read the words and write the correct word under each picture.

blob	brush	clip	crib
bless	branch	class	crab
blush	broom	cliff	crash
bleep	brim	clap	cross

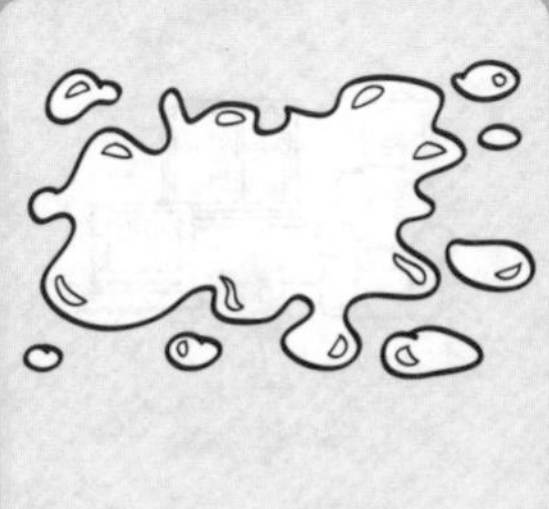
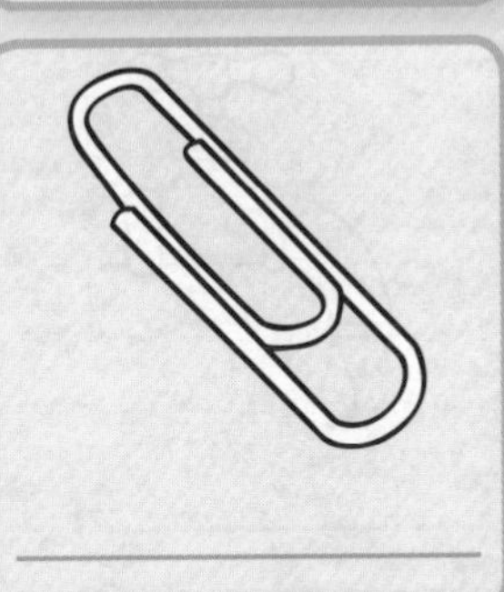

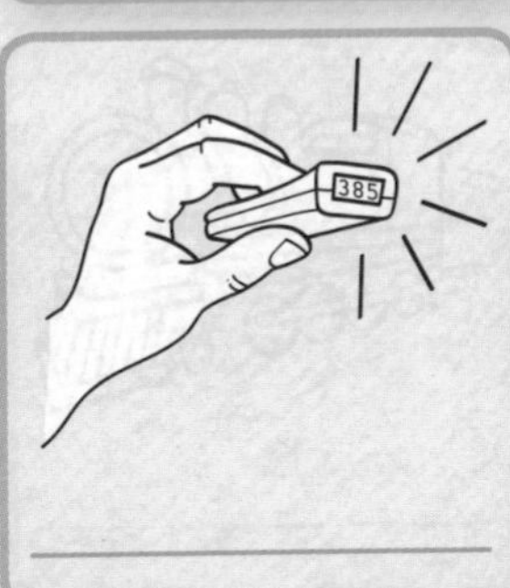

Objective: The child will be enabled to read and match simple words with the initial blends **bl**, **br**, **cl** and **cr**.

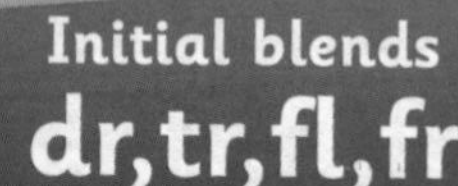

Say each word. Do you hear the dr, tr, fl or fr sound at the beginning of the word? Write the sound you hear.

Objective: The child will be enabled to identify items with the initial blends **dr**, **tr**, **fl** and **fr**.

Read the words and write the correct word under each picture.

tree	tram	trap	trim
drip	drum	drill	dress
drop	flag	flex	flash
flip flops	frill	frog	frizz

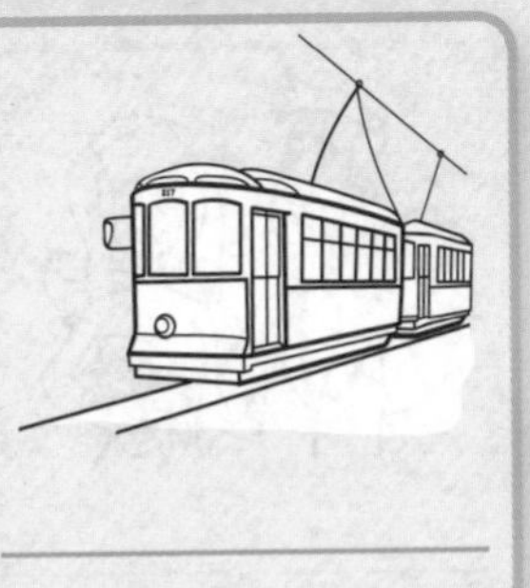
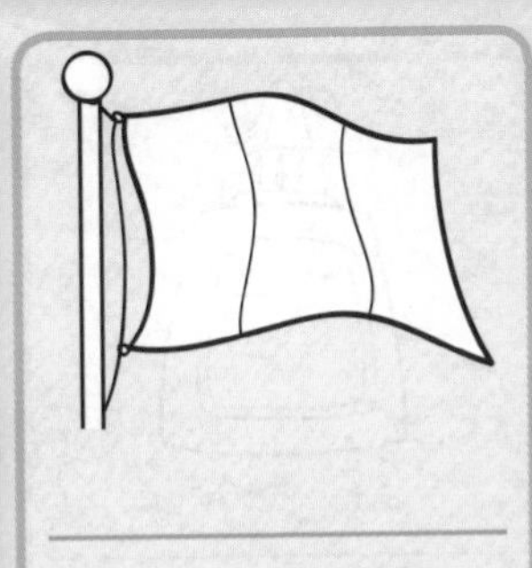

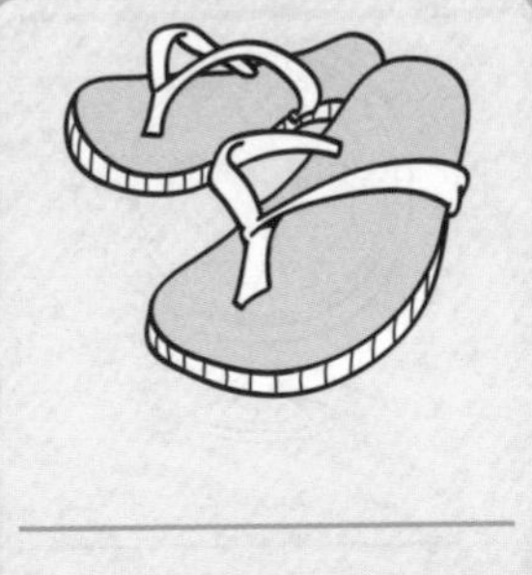

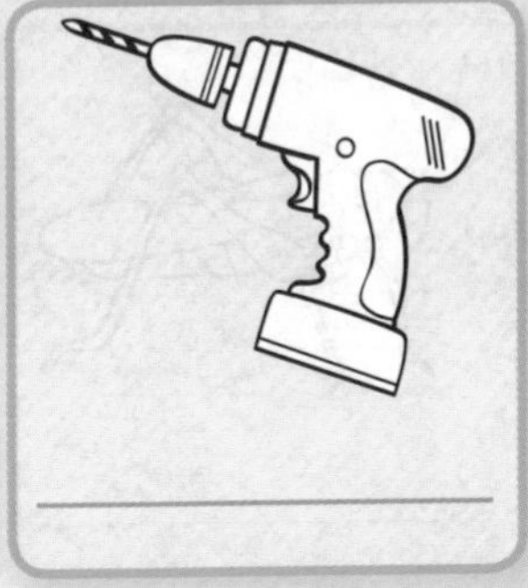

Objective: The child will be enabled to read and match simple words with the initial blends **dr**, **tr**, **fl** and **fr**.

Initial blends
gl, gr, pl, pr

Say each word. Do you hear the gl, gr, pl or pr sound at the beginning of the word? Write the sound you hear.

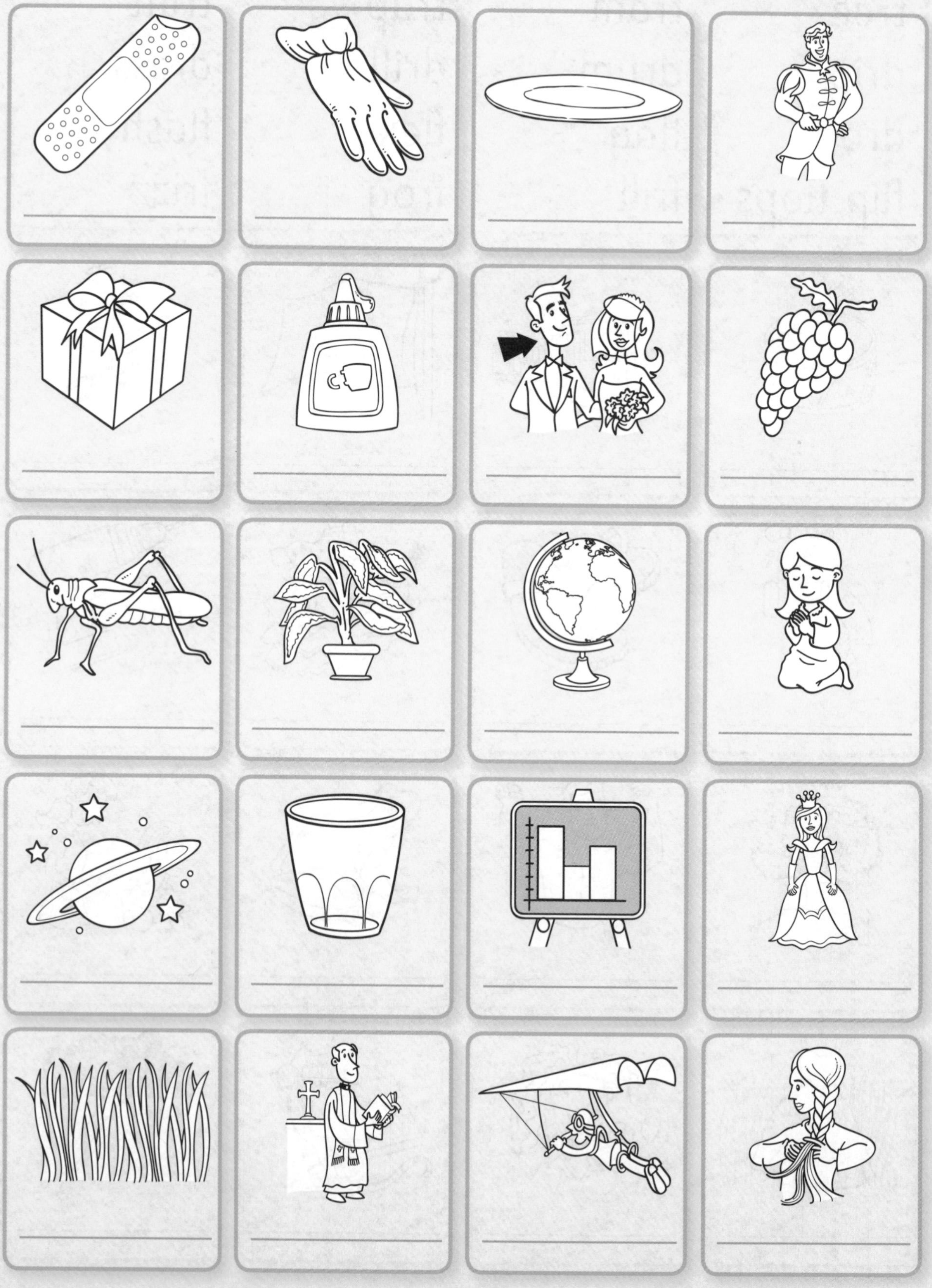

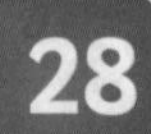

Objective: The child will be enabled to identify items with the initial blends **gl**, **gr**, **pl** and **pr**.

Read the words and write the correct word under each picture.

glass	glad	glasses	gran
grab	grub	grass	grin
grill	plug	plus	plum
plan	pram	press	prod

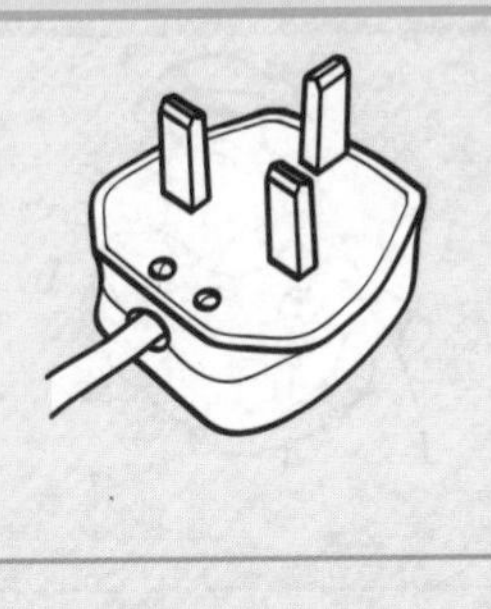

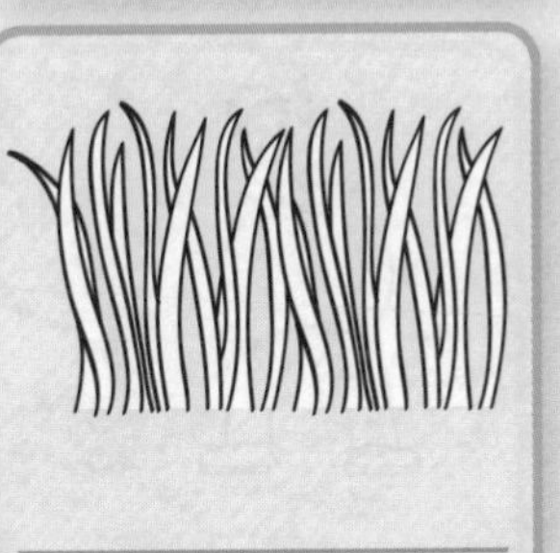

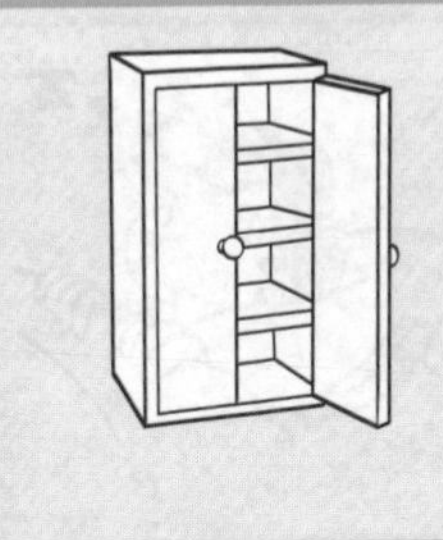

Objective: The child will be enabled to read and match simple words with the initial blends **gl**, **gr**, **pl** and **pr**.

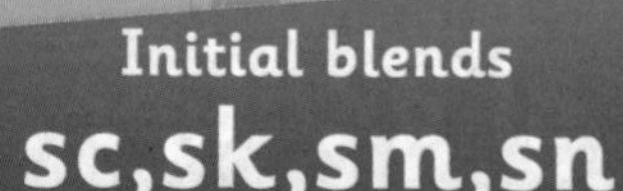

Say each word. Do you hear the sc, sk, sm or sn sound at the beginning of the word? Write the sound you hear.

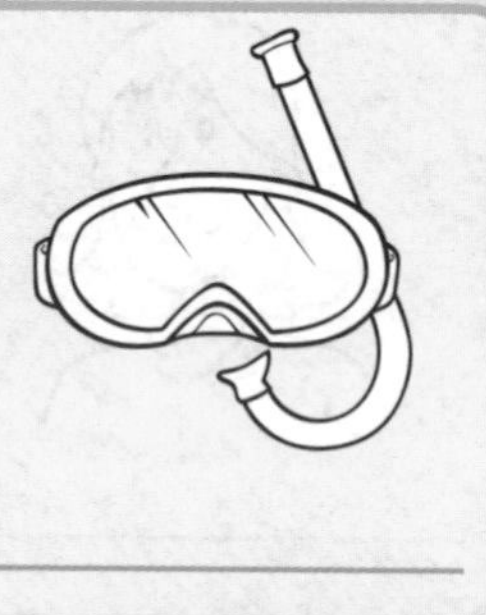

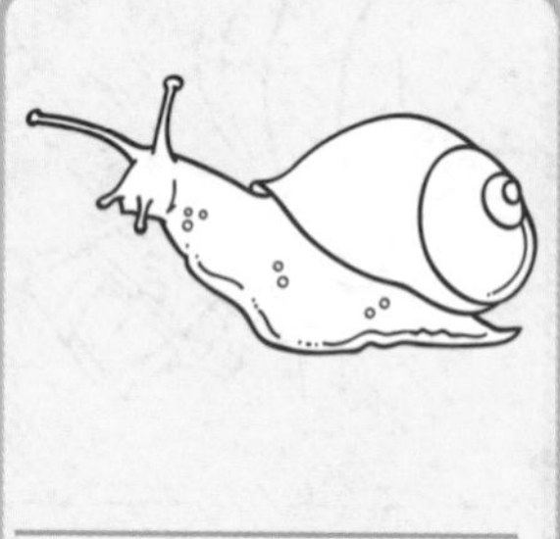

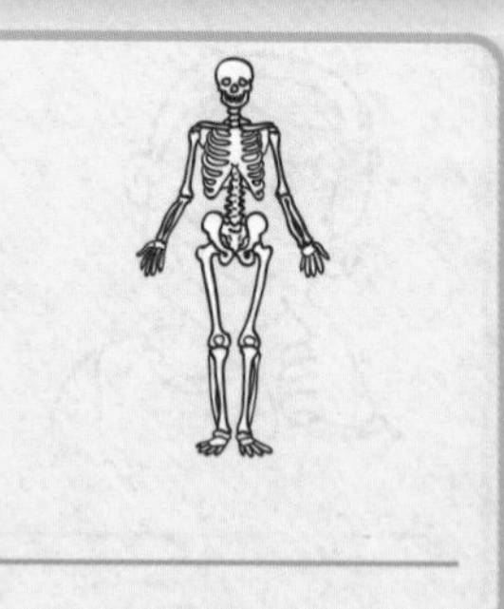

Objective: The child will be enabled to identify items with the initial blends **sc**, **sk**, **sm** and **sn**.

Read the words and write the correct word under each picture.

scab	scan	scat	sketch
skin	skull	skid	skip
small	smash	smell	snap
sniff	snip	snail	snob

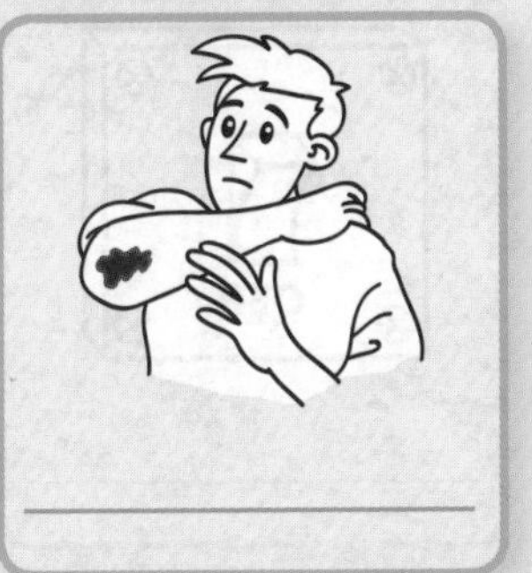

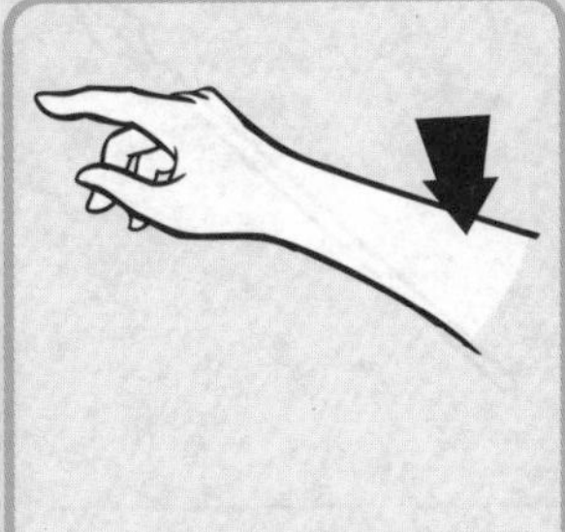

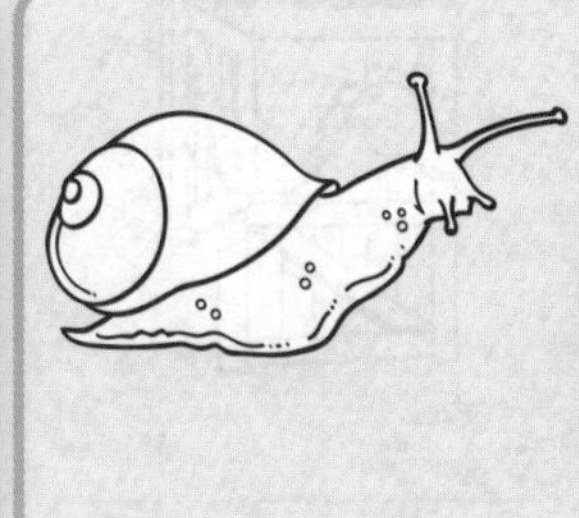
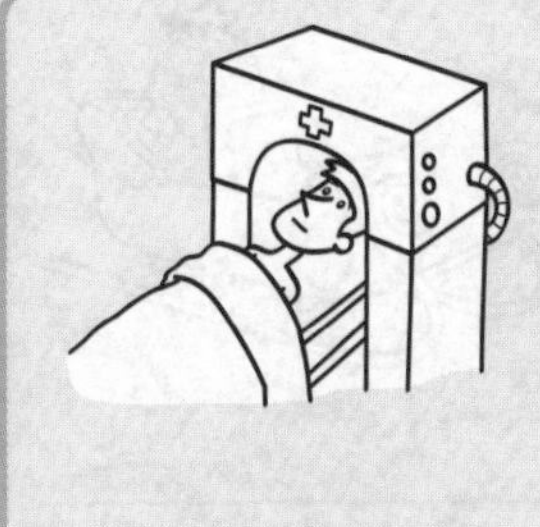

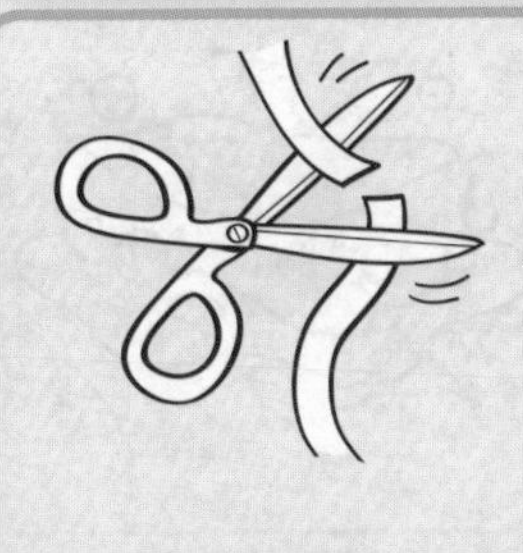

Objective: The child will be enabled to read and match simple words with the initial blends **sc**, **sk**, **sm** and **sn**.

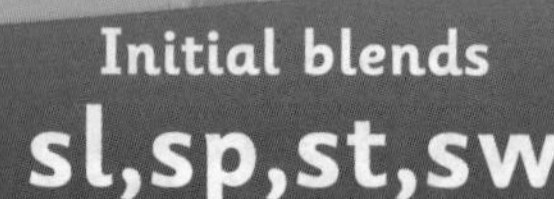

Say each word. Do you hear the sl, sp, st or sw sound at the beginning of the word? Write the sound you hear.

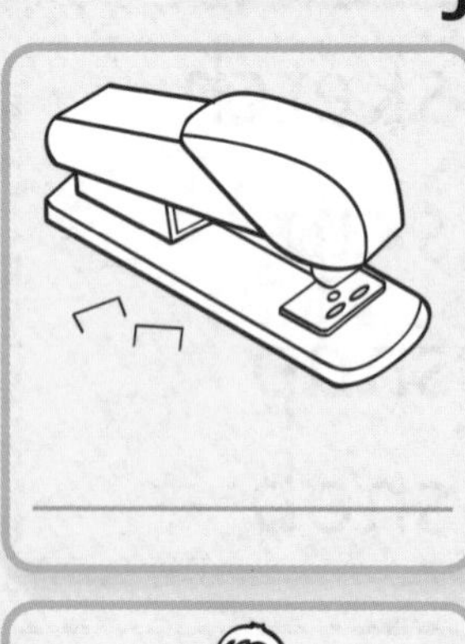

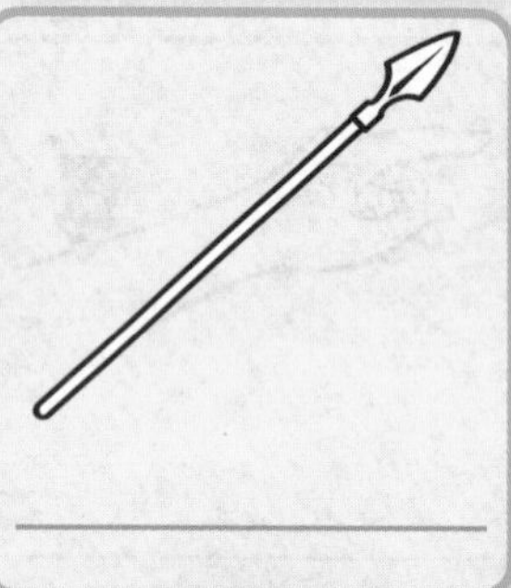
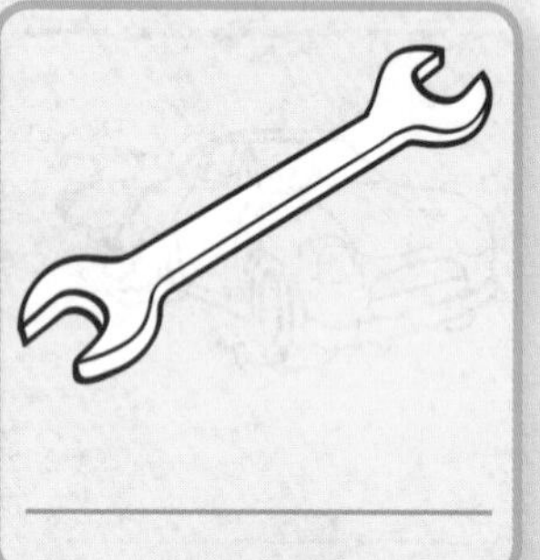

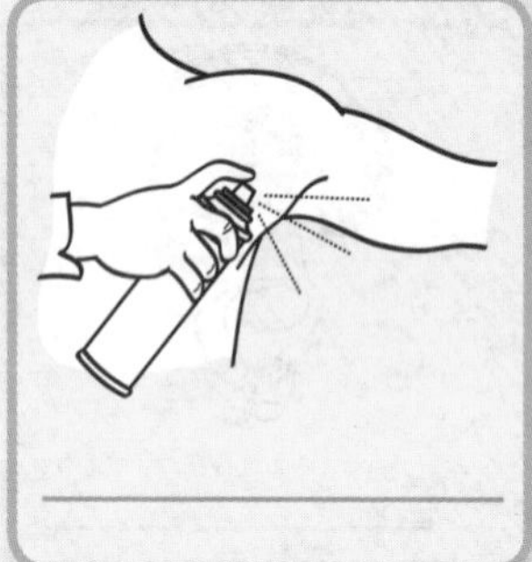

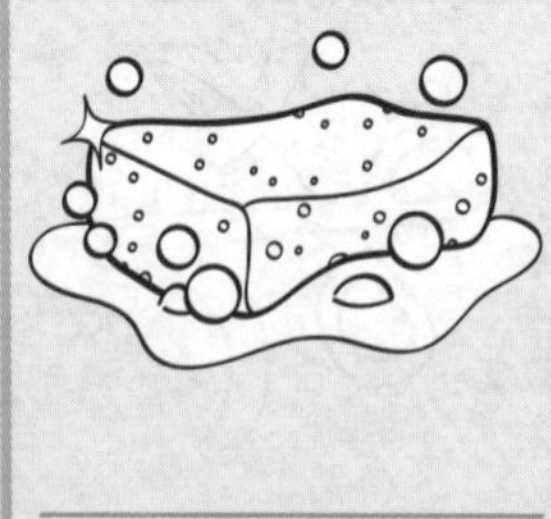

Objective: The child will be enabled to identify items with the initial blends **sl**, **sp**, **st** and **sw**.

Read the words and write the correct word under each picture.

slug	slip	slash	sleep
spill	spot	spell	spat
spin	stem	step	stop
stool	sweet	sweep	swim

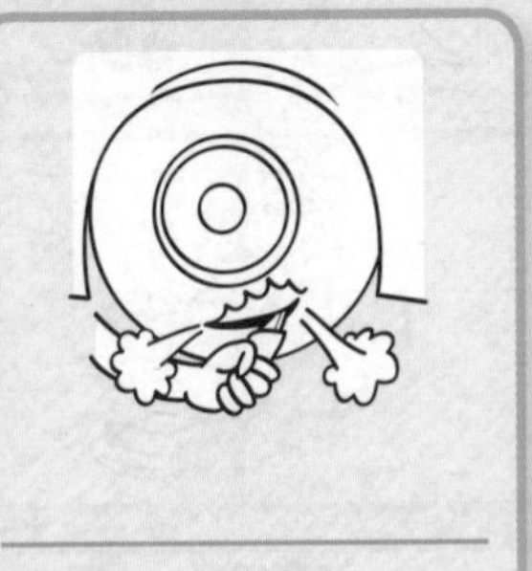

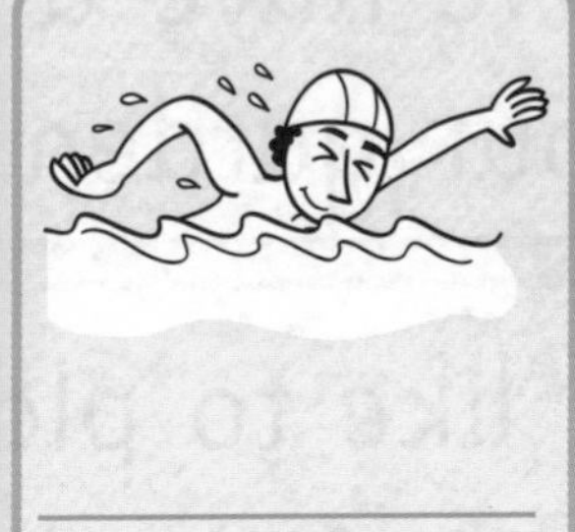

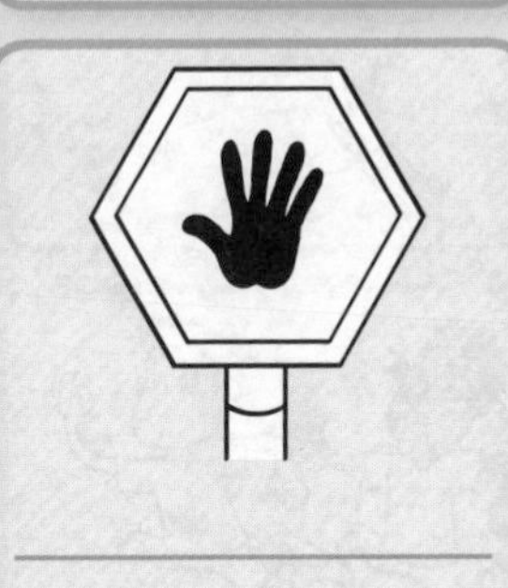

Objective: The child will be enabled to read and match simple words with the initial blends **sl**, **sp**, **st** and **sw**.

Read the sentences and fill in the correct word.

The duck likes to ______________.
(splash, spill)

The witch put a spell on the ______________. **(flag, frog)**

It is Dad's job to cut the ______________.
(grass, grab)

We have a big ______________ in our garden. **(tree, drip)**

I like to play ______________ with Pat. **(snap, snip)**

I have a red ______________.
(drop, dress)

The witch has a ______________.
(broom, brush)

I would like to be in the running ______________. **(clip, club)**

Objective: The child will be enabled to complete cloze procedure activities based on vocabulary with the initial blends **bl, br, cl, cr, dr, tr, fl, fr, gl, gr, pl, pr, sc, sk, sm, sn, sl, sp, st** and **sw.**

Read the sentences and fill in the correct word.

I ran up the ______________.
(cliff, clip)

My ______________ has glasses.
(gran, grab)

I have a ______________ on my leg.
(scan, scar)

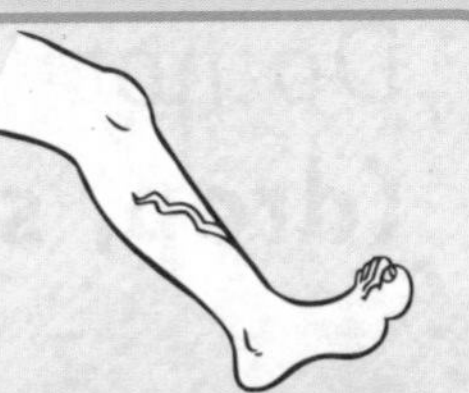

A crab can ______________.
(swan, swim)

The class gave the man a big ______________. **(clip, clap)**

Dad keeps his ______________ in the shed. **(drill, drip)**

Three ______________ three is six.
(plug, plus)

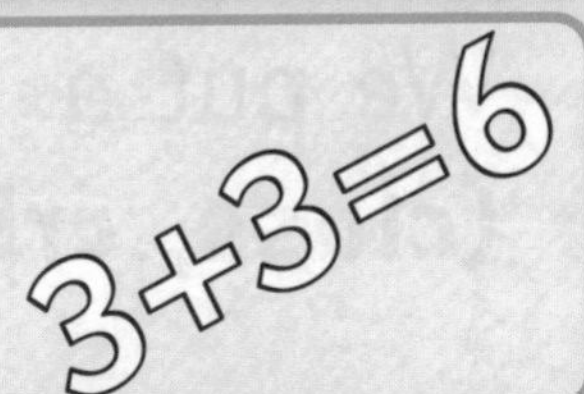

I put the doll in the ______________.
(press, pram)

Objective: The child will be enabled to complete cloze procedure activities based on vocabulary with the initial blends **bl, br, cl, cr, dr, tr, fl, fr, gl, gr, pl, pr, sc, sk, sm, sn, sl, sp, st** and **sw**.

Read the sentences and fill in the correct word.

Put all the ____________ in the ____________.
(glasses, press)

I saw a ____________ snail and ____________ on the path.
(small, slug)

Do not ____________ the cup, it will ____________.
(drop, smash)

The car got a ____________ and there was a big ____________.
(crash, skid)

I did not like the ____________ and ____________ it out.
(spat, sweet)

I was ____________ in bed and fell ____________.
(snug, asleep)

We put a ____________ up in our ____________.
(class, crib)

Do not ____________ on the slug in the ____________.
(step, grass)

Objective: The child will be enabled to complete cloze procedure activities based on vocabulary with the initial blends **bl, br, cl, cr, dr, tr, fl, fr, gl, gr, pl, pr, sc, sk, sm, sn, sl, sp, st** and **sw.**

Read the words and write the correct word under each picture.

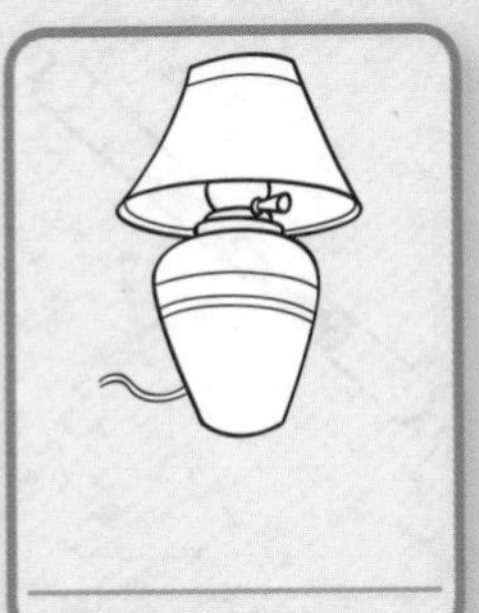

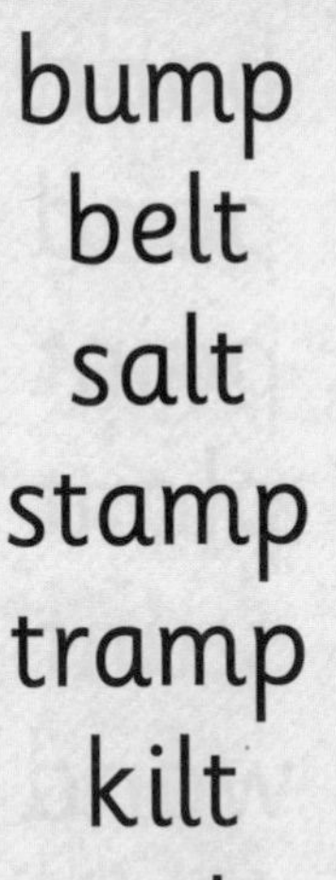

bump
belt
salt
stamp
tramp
kilt
quilt
lamp

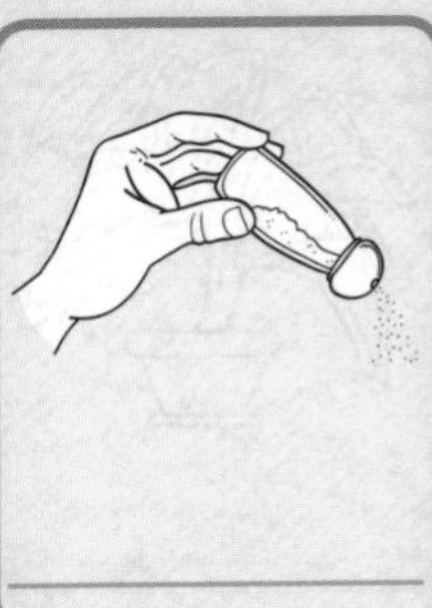

Read the sentences and fill in the correct word.

bump   stilts   kilt   cramp

The posh man had a ________.

I fell and got a ________.

I had lots of sweets and got a ________.

The tall man was on ________.

Objective: The child will be enabled to read simple words and sentences with the final blends **lt** and **mp**.

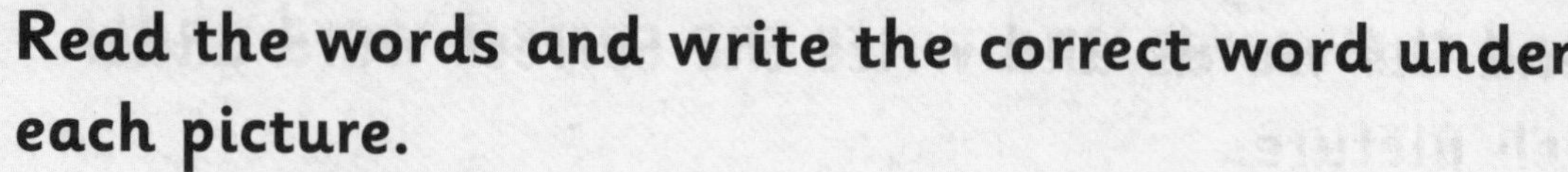

Read the words and write the correct word under each picture.

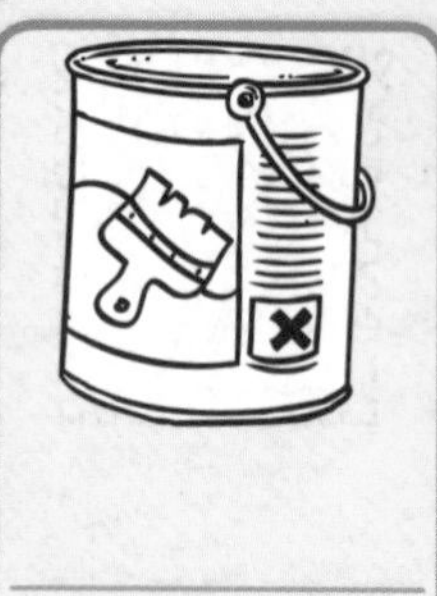

band
pond
paint
plant
stunt
wand
bent
send

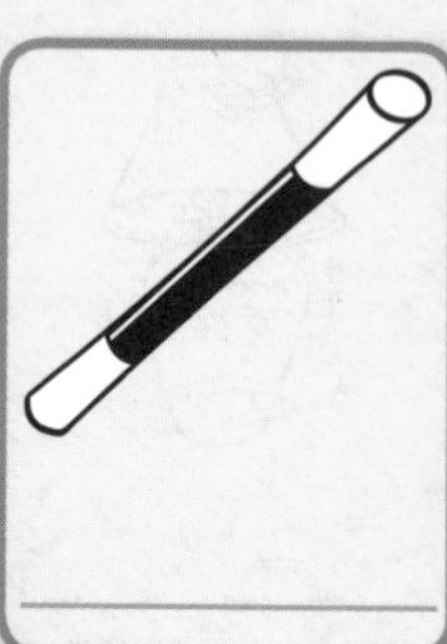

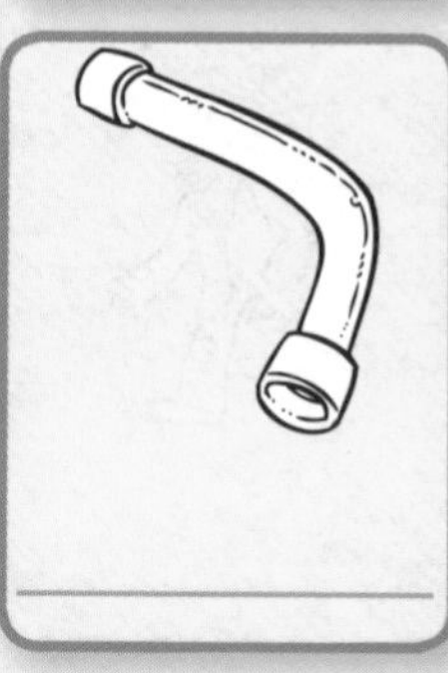

Read the sentences and fill in the correct word.

present sand hand tents

The crab hid in the __________.

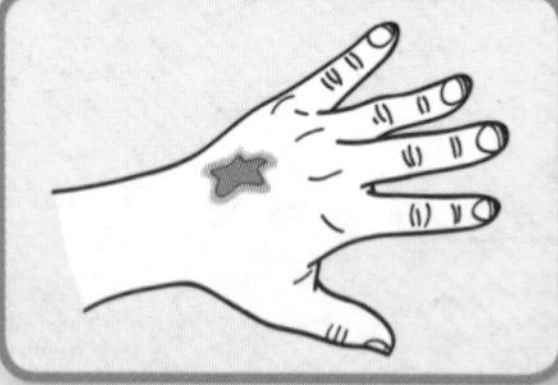

He has a scab on his __________.

There were lots of __________ in the camp.

Will you send me a big __________?

Objective: The child will be enabled to read simple words and sentences with the final blends **nd** and **nt**.

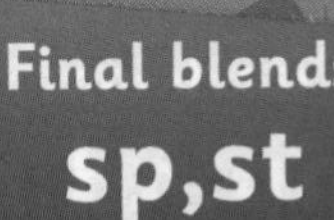

Read the words and write the correct word under each picture.

blast
frost
cast
clasp
crisp
gasp
nest
vest

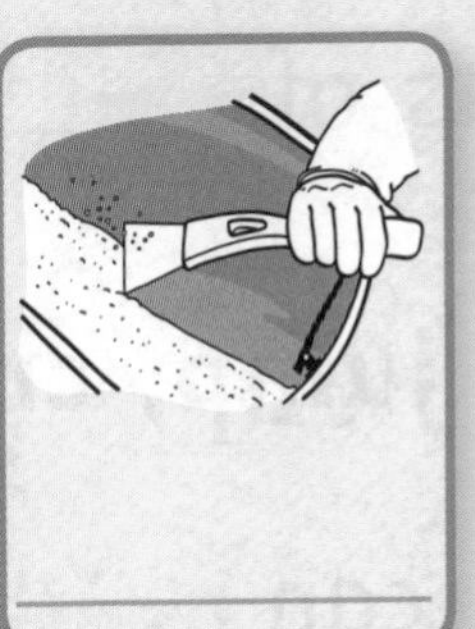

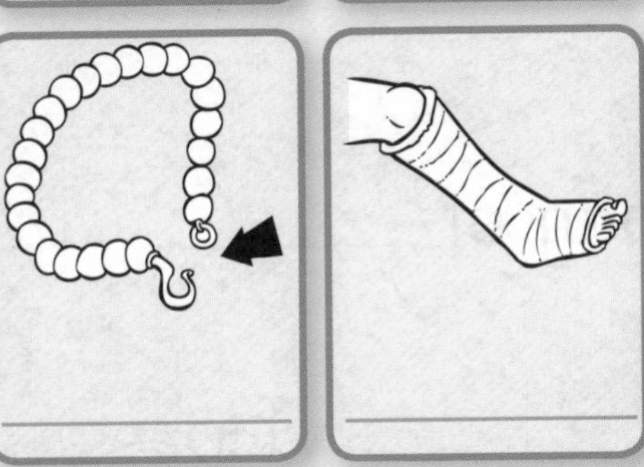

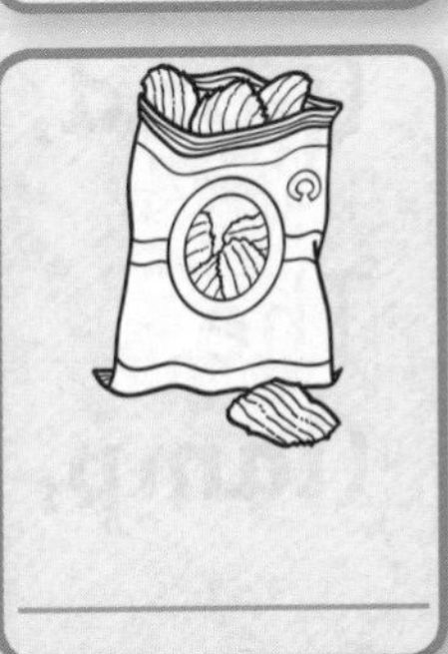

Read the sentences and fill in the correct word.

fist chest test crisps

We must pass a big ________ in class.

He hit me with his ________ and I got a lump.

I had lots of ________ and got a cramp.

Do not drop the ________.

Objective: The child will be enabled to read simple words and sentences with the final blends **sp** and **st**.

Read the sentences and fill in the correct word.

I had lots of ____________ and got a ____________.
(mints, jump, cramp)

The frog can ____________ into the ____________.
(pond, band, jump)

The ____________ man had a bag of ____________.
(lamp, crisps, plump)

I can ____________ and ____________ with my feet.
(stamp, tramp, jump)

The present got ____________ in the ____________.
(post, lost, frost)

I put a ____________ up in the ____________.
(camp, plant, tent)

I hit my ____________ and got a ____________.
(bump, hand, wand)

I got ____________ in the ____________ up on the cliff.
(nest, mist, lost)

Objective: The child will be enabled to complete cloze procedure activities based on vocabulary with the final blends **lt**, **mp**, **nd**, **nt**, **sp** and **st**.

Read the words and write the correct word under each picture.

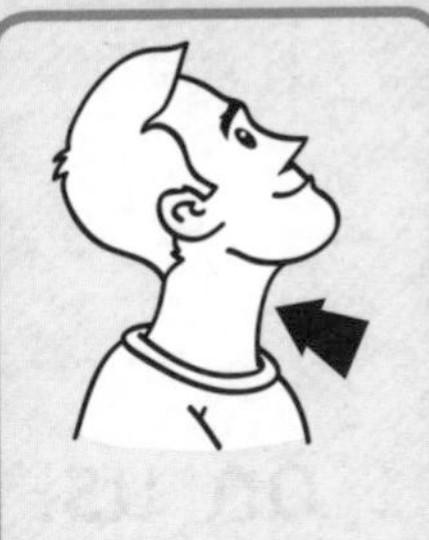

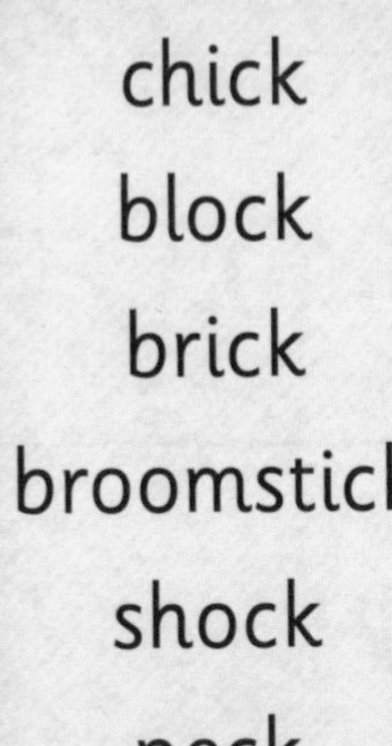

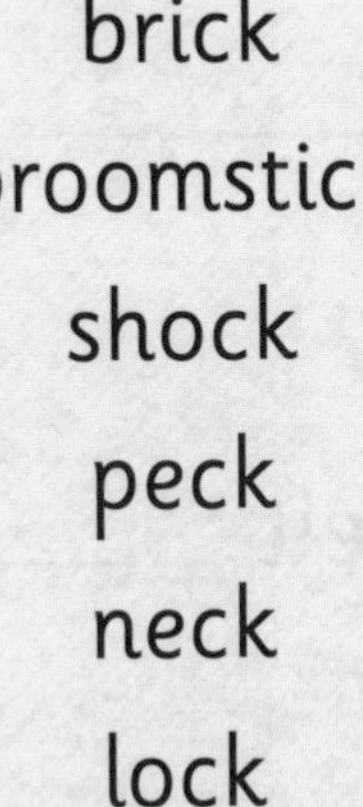

chick
block
brick
broomstick
shock
peck
neck
lock

Read the sentences and fill in the correct word.

muck quack stuck lick truck

The duck went ______________ in the pond.

The man can mend and fix the ______________.

I suck sweets and ______________ lollipops.

The car got ______________ in the ______________.

Objective: The child will be enabled to read simple words and sentences with the final blend **ck**.

Read the sentences and fill in the correct word.

Pick up that ____________.
(rock, rack)

Jack likes to play ____________ on us.
(tricks, tracks)

I had a cramp and felt ____________.
(sack, sick)

I have a lump and rash on my ____________.
(nick, neck)

Put the ____________ on the top shelf.
(cluck, clock)

That ____________ likes to ____________ me.
(peck, pick, duck)

Put on your ____________ ____________.
(socks, black, blink)

Will you ____________ the boxes in the ____________?
(pack, prick, truck)

Objective: The child will be enabled to complete cloze procedure activities based on vocabulary with the final blend **ck**.

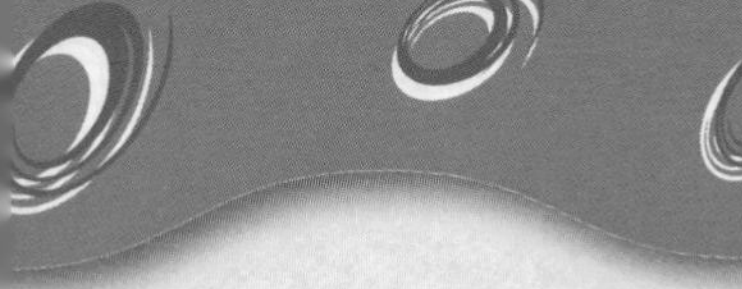

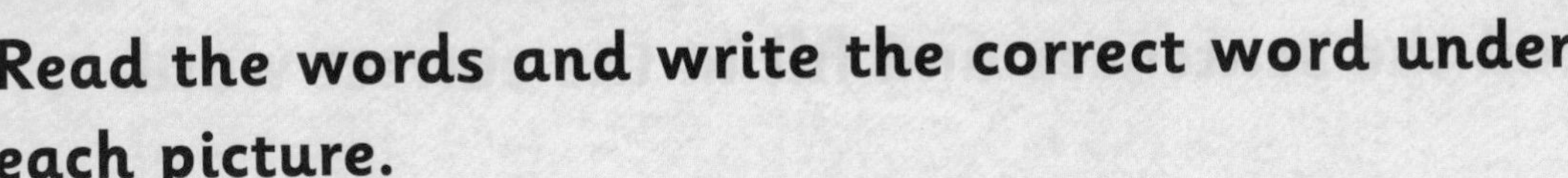

Read the words and write the correct word under each picture.

fang
sting
gang
hang
bang
lung
wing
ping pong

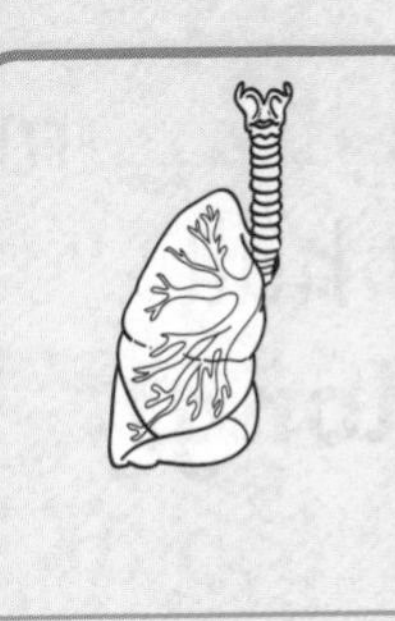

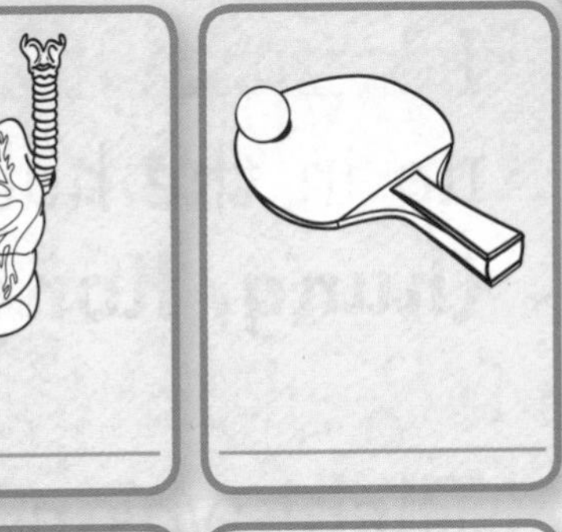

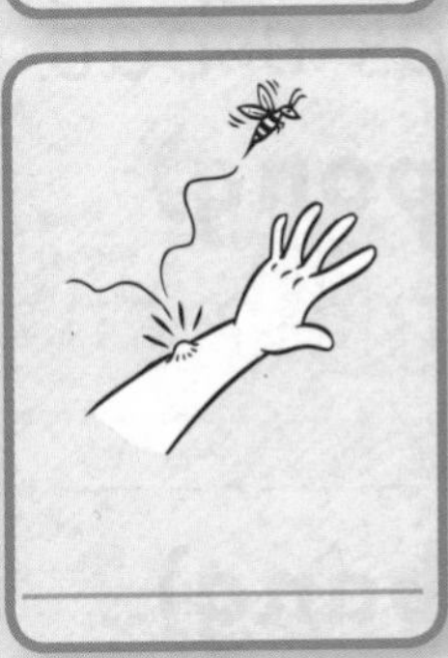

Read the sentences and fill in the correct word.

song ring king fangs

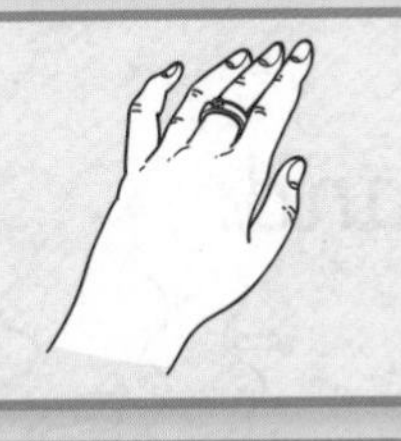

Mum has a gold ________.

The ________ went to meet the queen.

The man sang a long ________.

That dog has big ________.

Objective: The child will be enabled to read simple words and sentences with the final blend **ng**.

Read the sentences and fill in the correct word.

I ___________ my hat and coat up in the hall.
(hung, hong)

There was a bad ___________ off his socks.
(pang, pong)

I got a ___________ on my hand.
(bong, bang)

Pat likes to push me on the ___________.
(swung, swing)

Ben got a bad ___________ on his hand.
(sting, string)

I ___________ the rubbish in the bin.
(fang, flung)

I like to play ___________.
(ping, pong, pang)

My gran loves to ___________ a ___________.
(slung, song, sing)

Objective: The child will be enabled to complete cloze procedure activities based on vocabulary with the final blend **ng**.

     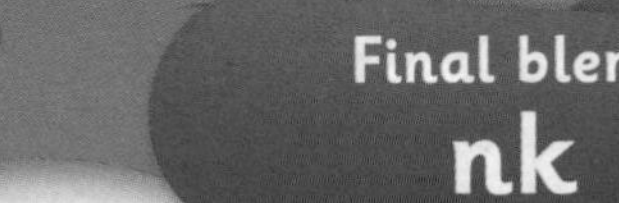

Read the words and write the correct word under each picture.

trunk
bank
tank
punk
plank
ink
drink
sink

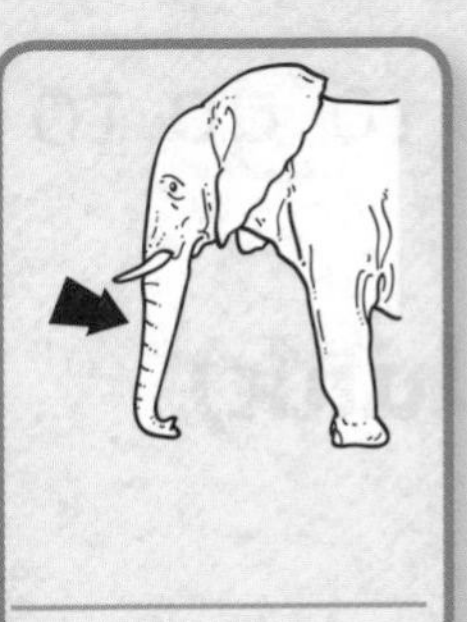 

Read the sentences and fill in the correct word.

junk   think   wink   bunk

I fell asleep in my ________ bed.

Put all of that ________ in the bin.

I ________ I can do it.

The jolly man likes to ________.

Objective: The child will be enabled to read simple words and sentences with the final blend **nk**.

Read the sentences and fill in the correct word.

Mum had to go to the __________ to get some cash.
(bank, blank)

I got a __________ and red dress as a present.
(punk, pink)

Will you wash your hands in the __________?
(sank, sink)

Dad put all the __________ in the shed.
(ink, junk)

In the USA a car boot is called a __________.
(trunk, think)

I have a set of __________ beds in my room.
(bank, bunk)

That __________ likes to play __________.
(pranks, punk, pink)

I __________ I had too many sweets and __________ food.
(thank, junk, think)

Objective: The child will be enabled to complete cloze procedure activities based on vocabulary with the final blend **nk**.

Magic E is magic! It sends magic over to the letter a and makes it say its name!

tap + e → tap e

can + e → can e

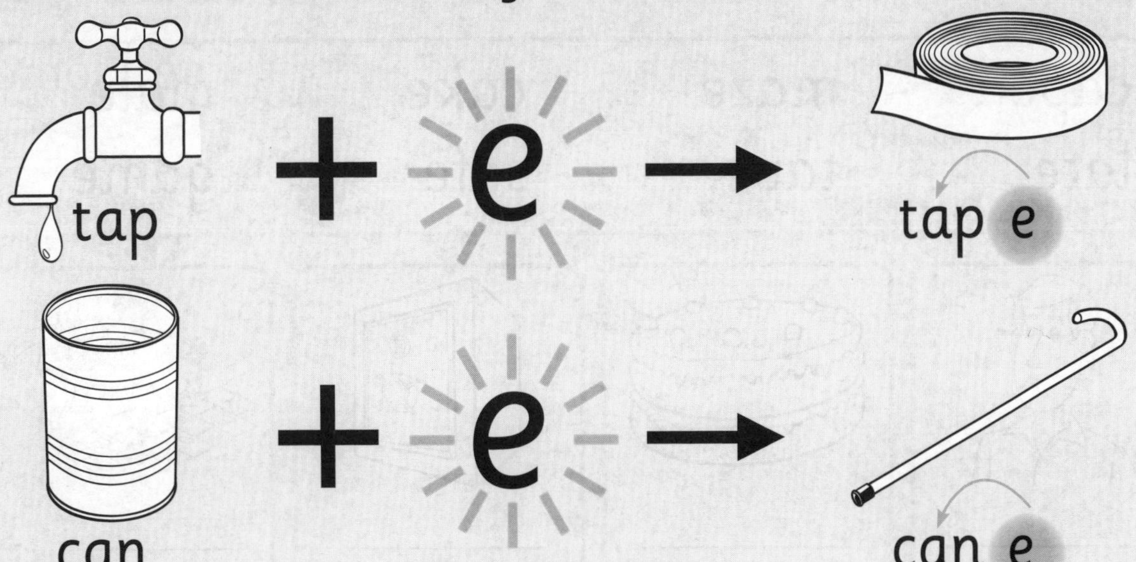

Say each word. Is it a Magic e word? Circle yes or no.

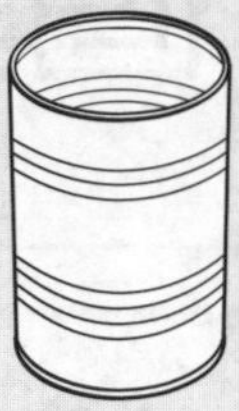

yes no

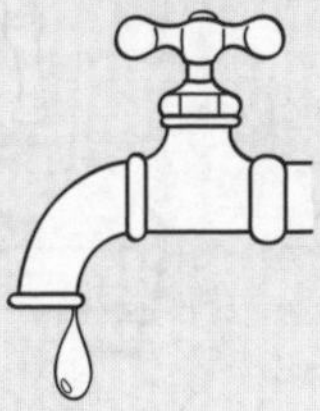

yes no

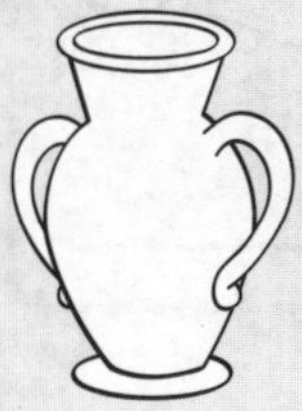

yes no

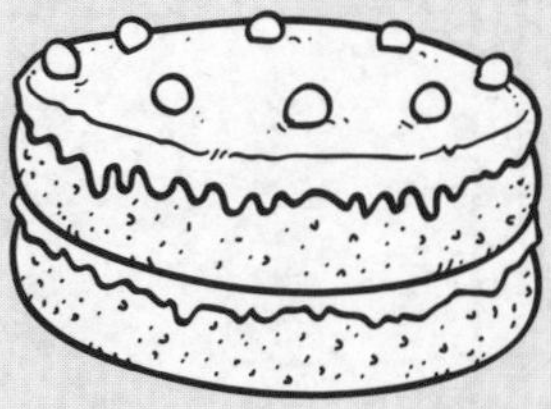

yes no

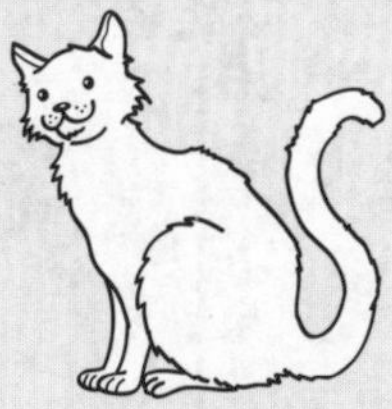

yes no

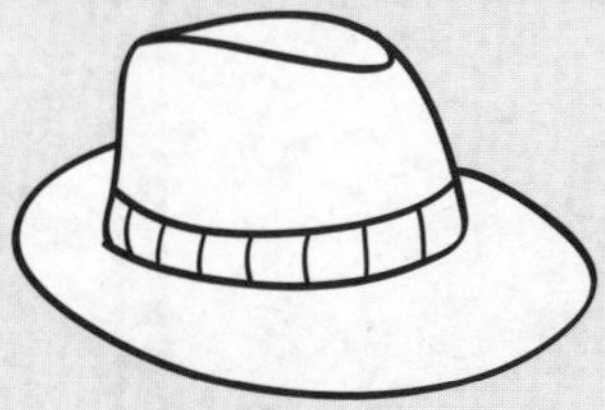

yes no

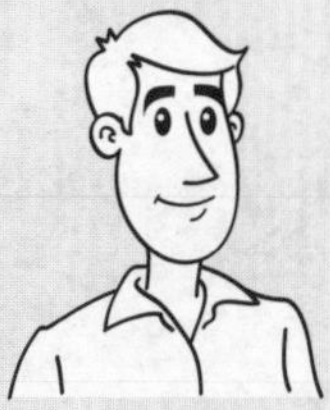

yes no

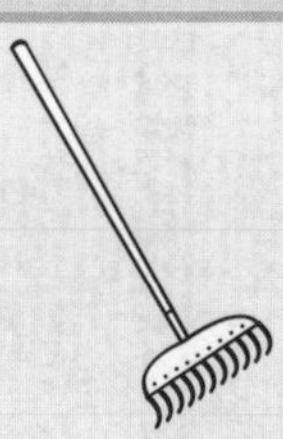

yes no

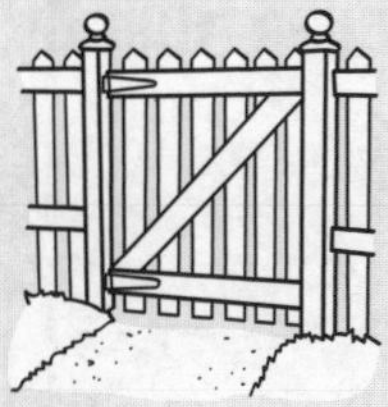

yes no

Objective: The child will be enabled to identify the **Magic E** rule with **a** and identify if a word is a **Magic E** word.

Read the words and write the correct word under each picture.

cape	maze	cake	male
late	tape	safe	game

 ________

 ________

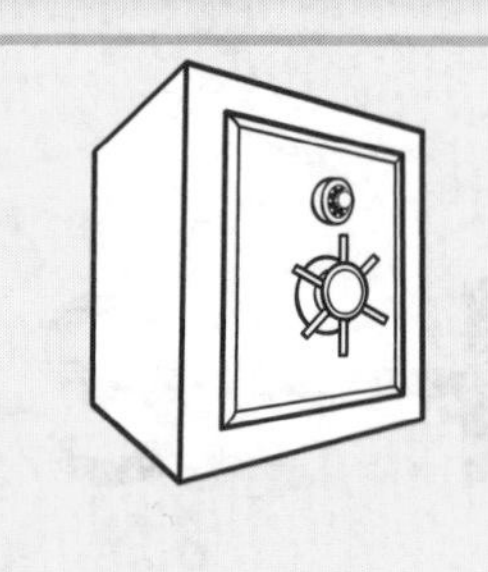 ________

 ________

 ________

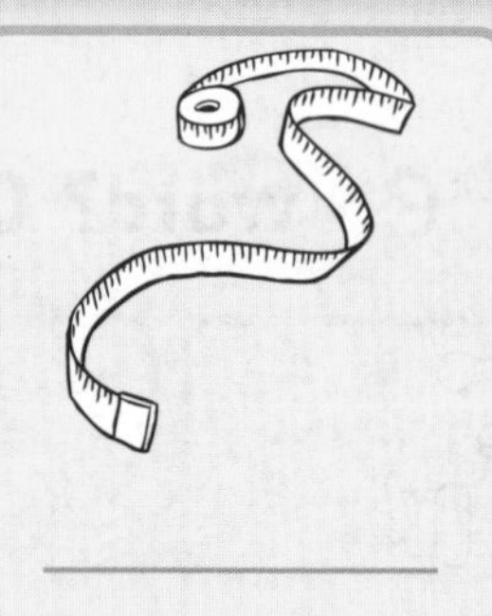 ________

 ________

 ________

Read the words and draw the correct picture.

cave	case	gate	cane
rake	name	vase	sale

Objective: The child will be enabled to identify the **Magic E** rule and read words containing **Magic E** with a.

Read the sentences and fill in the correct word.

	I like to ____________ buns.	bake bale
	We went for a swim in the ____________.	lake lane
	Can you open the ____________?	gape gate
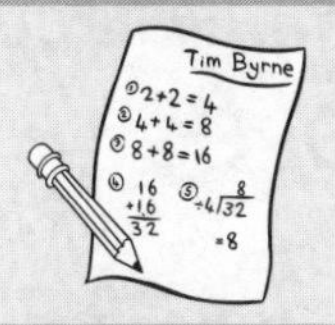	Put your name on the top of the ____________.	page pane
	When I was sick I was very ____________.	pale page
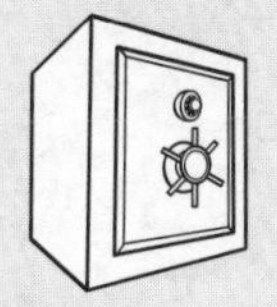	Put the cash in the ____________.	sale safe
	Did you pack your ____________?	case cape
	I got the pink dress in the ____________.	save sale
	Did he nick the cash from the ____________?	safe sale
	I made a yummy ____________ with Gran.	cake case

Objective: The child will be enabled to complete cloze procedure activities based on vocabulary containing **Magic E** with a.

Magic E is magic! It sends magic over to the letter i and makes it say its name!

pin + e → pine

pip + e → pipe

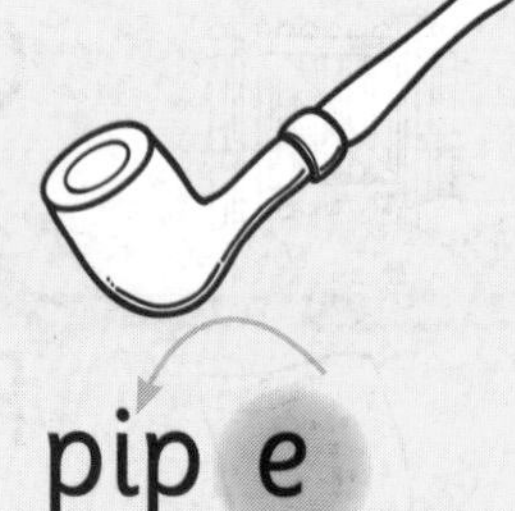

Say each word. Is it a Magic e word? Circle yes or no.

 yes no	 yes no	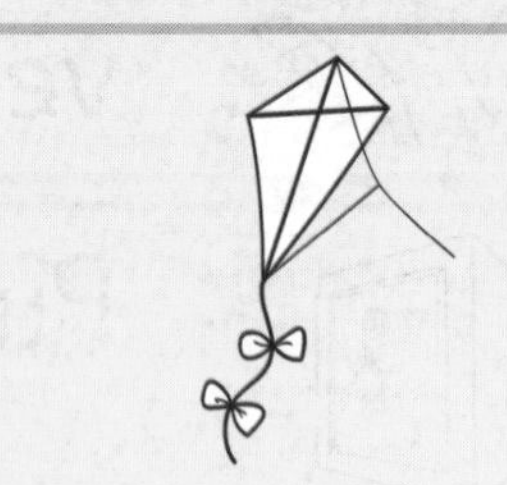 yes no
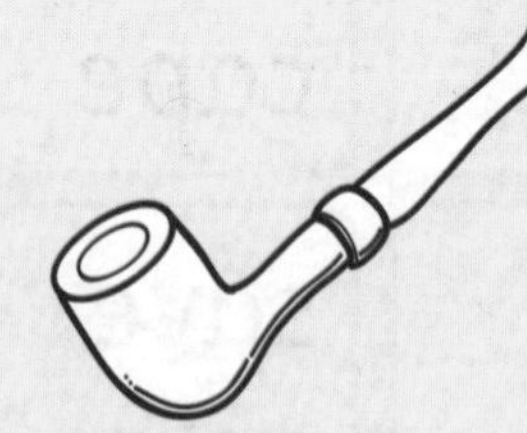 yes no	 yes no	 yes no
 yes no	 yes no	 yes no

Objective: The child will be enabled to identify the **Magic E** rule with **i** and identify if a word is a **Magic E** word.

Read the words and write the correct word under each picture.

pipe	time	wife	dive
wire	wine	mime	hike

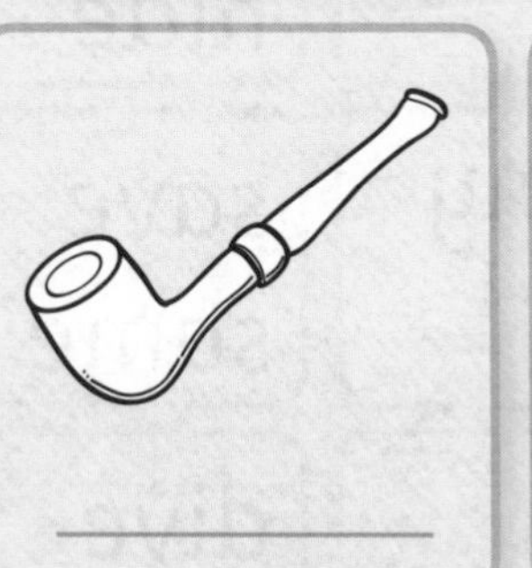

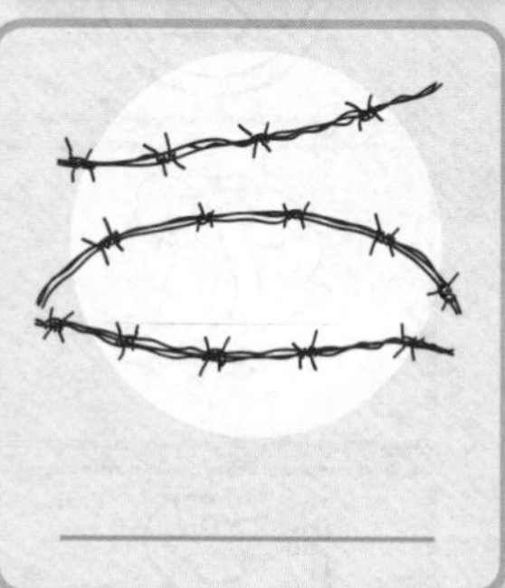

Read the words and draw the correct picture.

five	fire	hive	nine
kite	bike	line	fire

Objective: The child will be enabled to identify the **Magic E** rule with **i** and read words containing **Magic E** with **i**.

Read the sentences and fill in the correct word.

	I fell off my __________ and got a bump.	bite bike
	We went up the cliff on a big __________.	hike hide
	I will __________ all my cash in the bank.	save same
	You cannot swim or __________ in the pond.	dive date
	Can you sweep and __________ the floor?	wife wipe
	Dad likes to drink red __________.	wine wise
	There is a big __________ of books in my class.	pine pile
	At __________ o'clock I go to bed.	nine nice
	We have a bee __________ in our garden.	hive hike
	Did you __________ the chest in the shed?	hive hide

Objective: The child will be enabled to complete cloze procedure activities based on vocabulary containing **Magic E** with **i**.

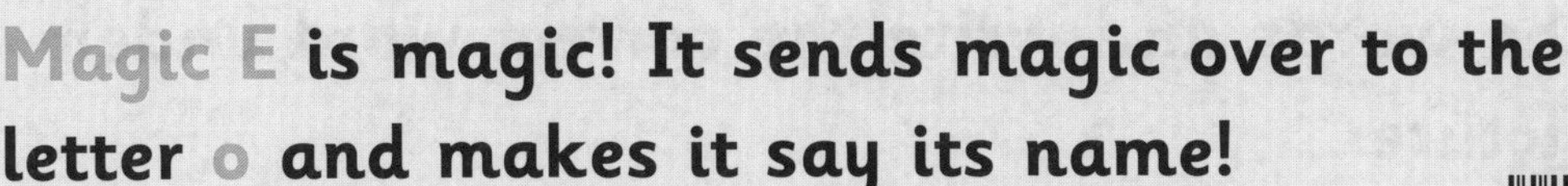

Magic E is magic! It sends magic over to the letter o and makes it say its name!

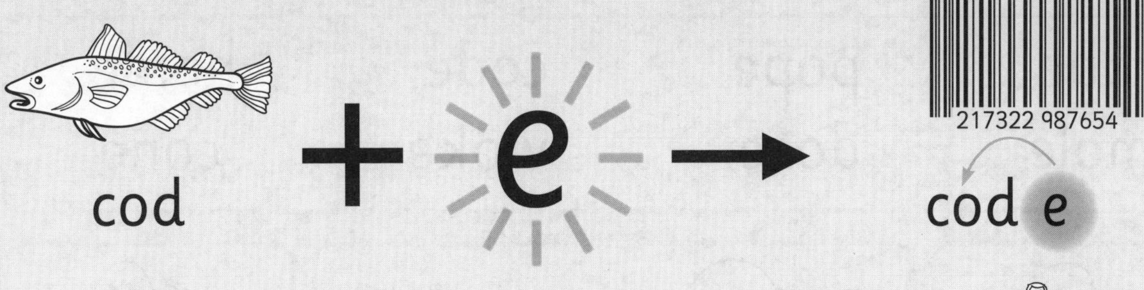

cod + e → cod e

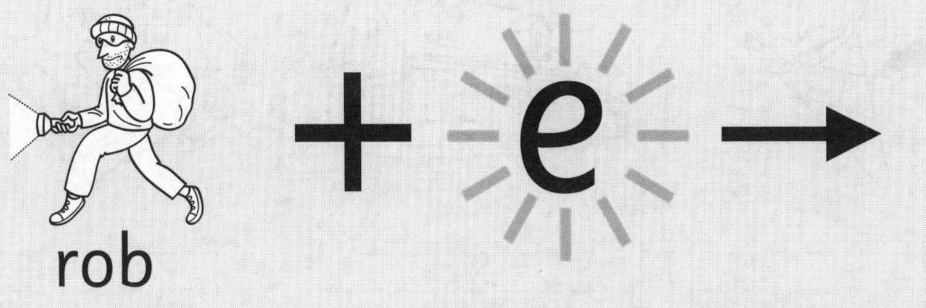

rob + e → rob e

Say each word. Is it a Magic e word? Circle yes or no.

 yes no	  yes no	 yes no
 yes no	 yes no	 yes no
 yes no	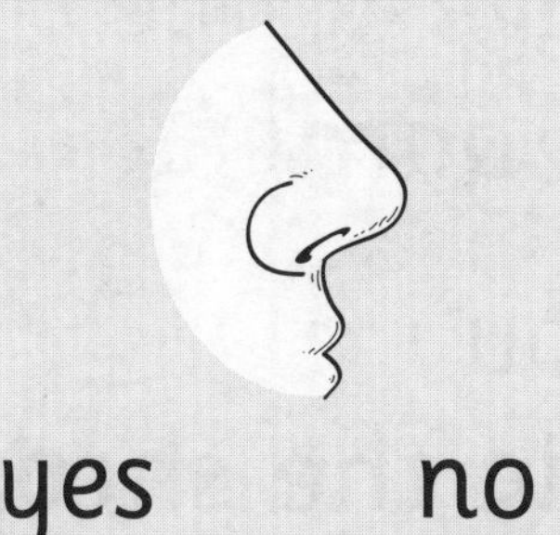 yes no	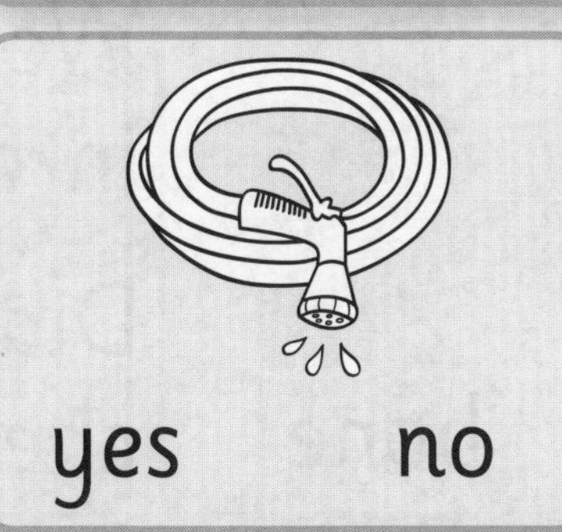 yes no

Objective: The child will be enabled to identify the **Magic E** rule with **o** and identify if a word is a **Magic E** word.

Read the words and write the correct word under each picture.

robe	pope	code	home
mole	doze	woke	cone

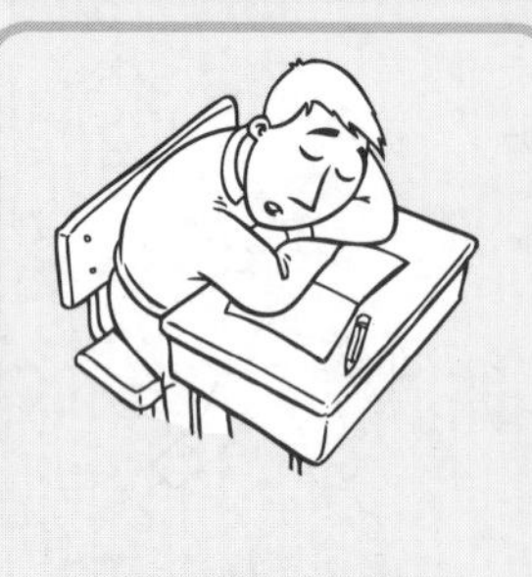

Read the words and draw the correct picture.

note	nose	rose	home
bone	hole	rope	pole

Objective: The child will be enabled to identify the **Magic E** rule with **o** and read words containing **Magic E** with **o**.

Read the sentences and fill in the correct word.

	Do you have the ________ to open the safe?	coke code
	We put a flag on the ________.	pole pose
	I ________ up at nine o'clock.	yoke woke
	I had a drink of ________ at lunch.	coke code
	When I was sick I had a runny ________.	note nose
	I went to pick a ________ for my gran.	robe rose
	I was snug in my bath ________.	robe rode
	The witch likes to ________ you with her wand.	poke pose
	I was snug in bed and began to ________.	dose doze
	The dog dug up a ________ in the garden.	bone cone

Objective: The child will be enabled to complete cloze procedure activities based on vocabulary containing **Magic E** with **o**.

Magic E is magic! It sends magic over to the letter u and makes it say its name!

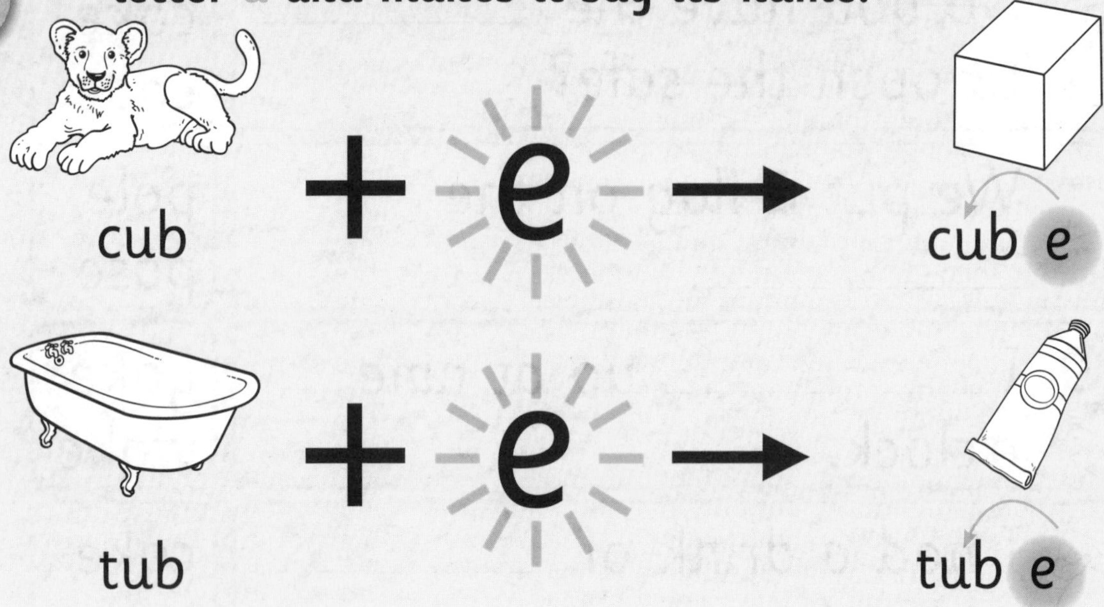

Say each word. Is it a Magic e word? Circle yes or no.

Objective: The child will be enabled to identify the **Magic E** rule with **u** and identify if a word is a **Magic E** word.

Read the words and write the correct word under each picture.

tube	dude	cute	nude
rude	tune	rule	duke

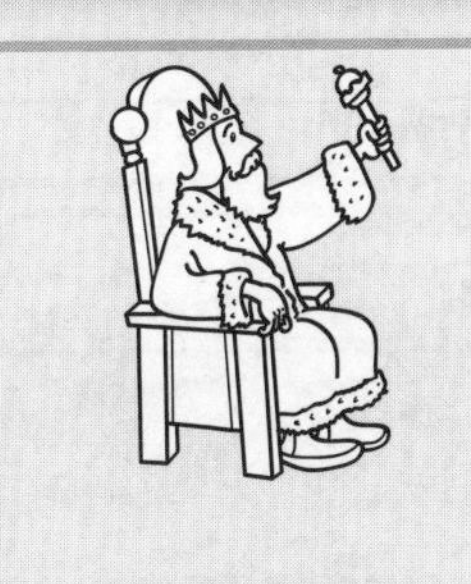

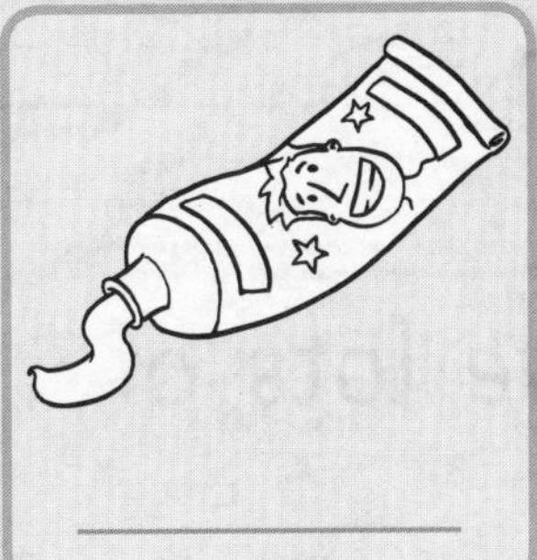

Read the words and draw the correct picture.

cube	mule	fuse	June
dune	ruler	rude	mute

Objective: The child will be enabled to identify the **Magic E** rule with **u** and read words containing **Magic E** with **u**.

Read the sentences and fill in the correct word.

	That pet cat is very ________.	cute cube
	I was very hot so I got an ice ________ for my drink.	cute cube
	That ________ likes to kick.	mole mule
	Put the telly on ________.	mote mute
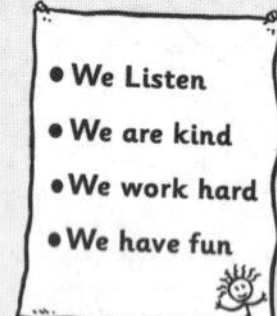	In class we have lots of ________.	roles rules
	We sang a ________ for the man.	tube tune
	We had a picnic in the sand ________.	dune duke
	The man was very ________.	rude rule
	We will go on a trip with our class in ________.	June dude

Objective: The child will be enabled to complete cloze procedure activities based on vocabulary containing **Magic E** with **u**.

Read the words and write the correct word under each picture.

blade
choke
plane
crane
shape
grape
globe
bride
snake
frame
grave
brake
slide
drive
slave

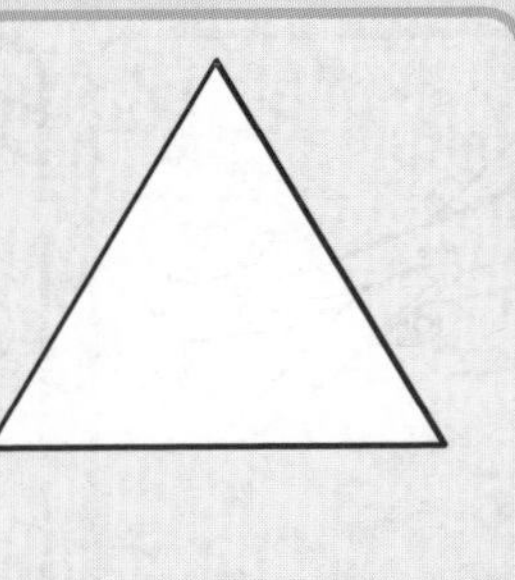

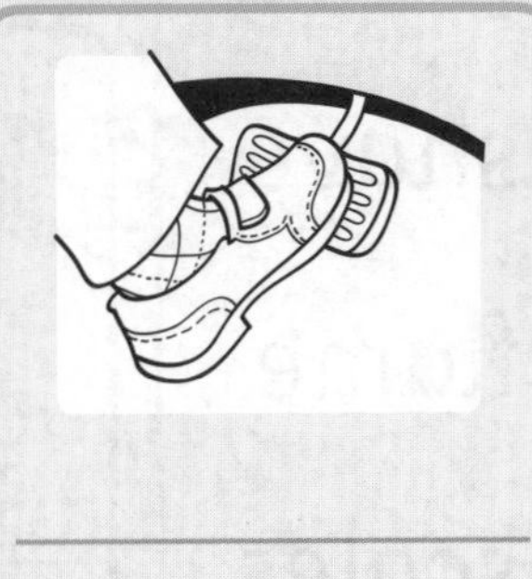

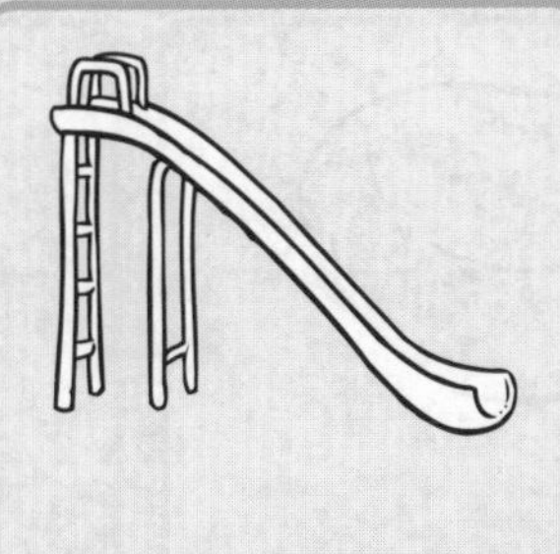

Objective: The child will be enabled to read and match simple words containing **Magic E** with **a**, **i**, **o**, **u** and initial blends.

Read the words and write the correct word under each picture.

flake
skate
plate
shave
flame
scales
spade
smoke
scone
plane
spike
slime
chase
stone
whale

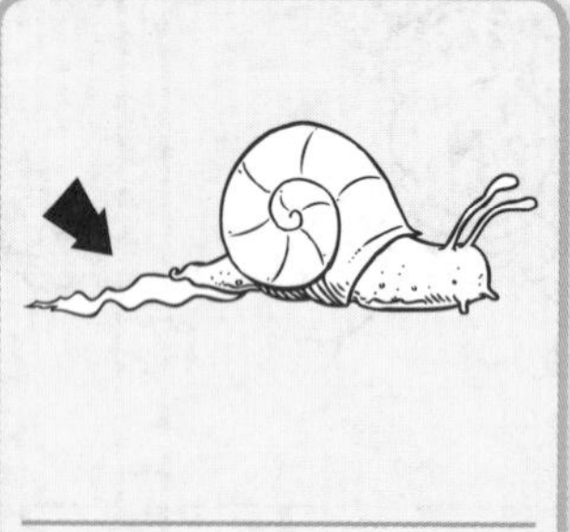

Objective: The child will be enabled to read and match simple words containing **Magic E** with **a**, **i**, **o**, **u** and initial blends.

Read the sentences and fill in the correct word.

That boy was very ______________ when he fell.
(brake, brave)

The bride wore a ______________ dress.
(whine, white)

We had to trace lots of ______________ in class.
(shaves, shapes)

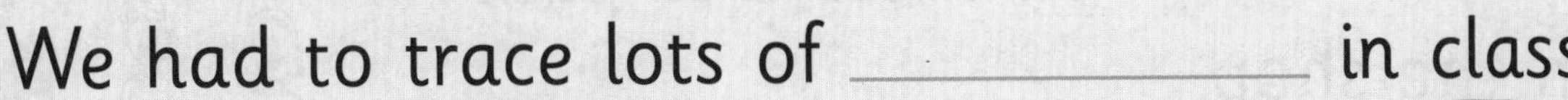

A small child can ______________ on a small nut.
(choke, chose)

I had bananas and ______________ for my snack today.
(grapes, grazes)

My dad loves to go out for a ______________ in his car.
(drive, drape)

Gran put the pot on the ______________.
(stone, stove)

The slug left a path of ______________ behind him.
(slide, slime)

Objective: The child will be enabled to complete cloze procedure activities based on vocabulary containing **Magic E** with blends.

Read the sentences and fill in the correct word.

The boy broke the __________.
(close, globe)

I can play a tune on the __________.
(fluke, flute)

I __________ a red dress and pink top in the shop.
(chose, choke)

I do not like to drink milk __________.
(snakes, shakes)

That small boy can ride a __________ very fast.
(trike, tribe)

I won a __________ when I won the race.
(pride, prize)

I had a glass of milk and a __________ with jam.
(scone, stone)

Put the bucket and __________ in the shed.
(spade, shake)

Objective: The child will be enabled to complete cloze procedure activities based on vocabulary containing **Magic E** with blends.

Read the sentences and fill in the correct word.

The ____________ man saved the cat from the tree top.
(brave, brake)

I had a big ______________ on my face when I won the prize.
(snake, smile)

Dad put a ______________ up on the wall.
(frame, flame)

I would like to drive a ______________ when I am big.
(crane, crate)

A cat ran out in front of the car and Dad had to slam on the ____________.
(brakes, braves)

There were lots of ____________ in glass boxes in the zoo.
(snakes, shakes)

That man ______________ the cash from the safe.
(stone, stole)

We have a big ______________ in our classroom.
(grove, globe)

Objective: The child will be enabled to complete cloze procedure activities based on vocabulary containing **Magic E** with blends.

Read the words and write the correct word under each picture.

cheese	teeth	breeze	geese
sheep	wheel	freeze	canteen

Read the sentences and fill in the correct word.

steep seeds tweet coffee

It was very ______________ when we went up to the cliff.

I like to eat toffees when I drink my ______________.

The duck went 'Quack' and the chick went '______________'.

I can plant some ______________ in a pot.

Objective: The child will be enabled to identify that the letters **ee** make the **/ee/** sound and read simple words and sentences with **ee**.

Read the words and write the correct word under each picture.

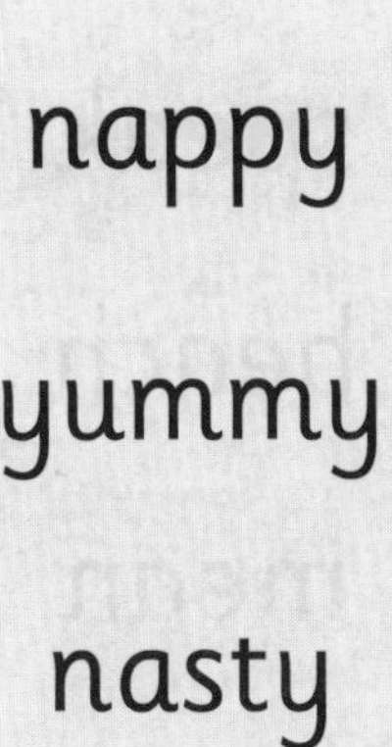
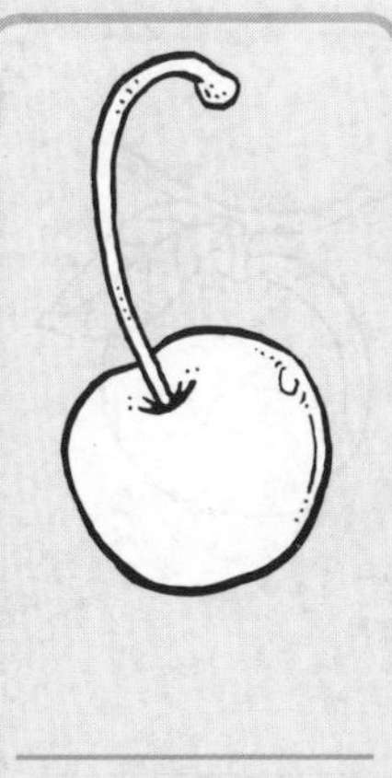

nappy

yummy

nasty

jelly

ferry

holly

buggy

telly

cherry

sticky

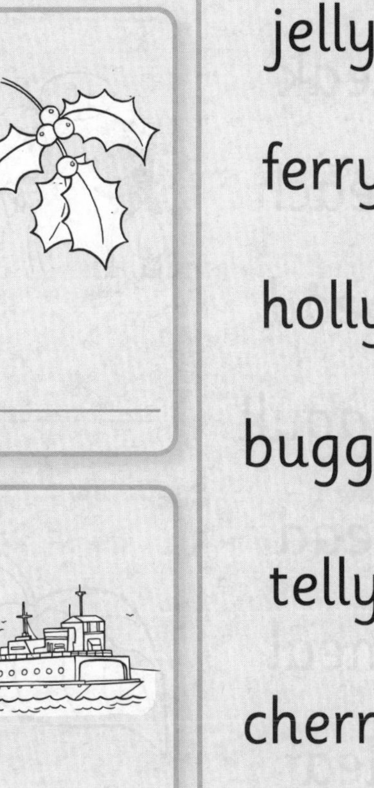

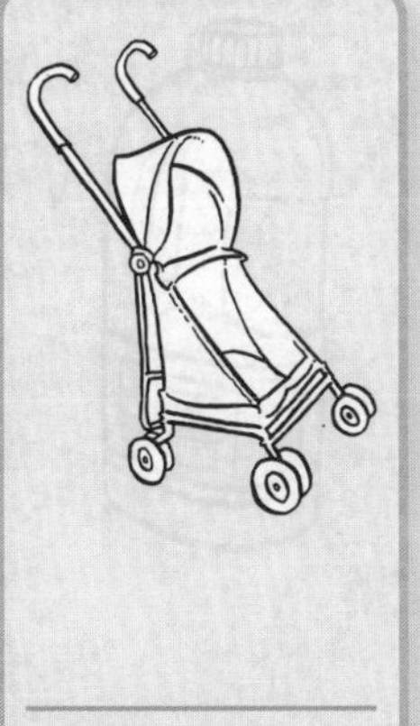
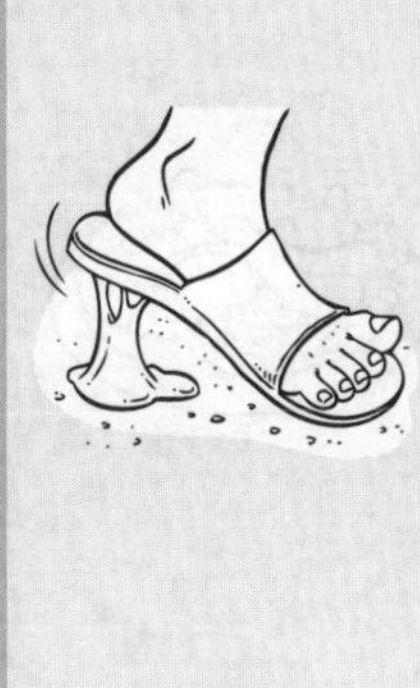

Objective: The child will be enabled to identify that the letter **y** at the end of a word can make the **/ee/** sound and read simple words with **y** at the end.

Read the words and write the correct word under each picture.

We all make the ee sound.

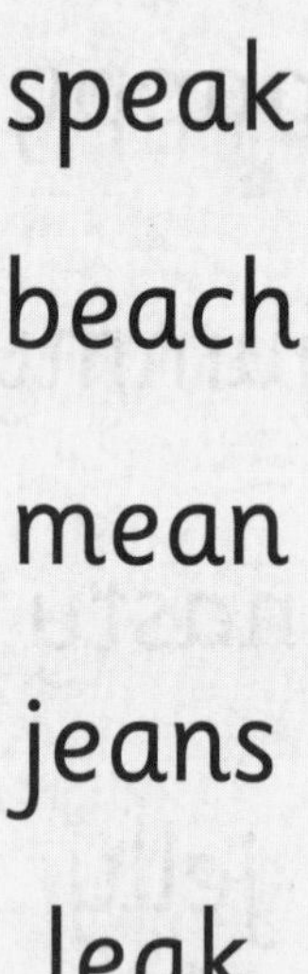

speak

beach

mean

jeans

leak

peach

bead

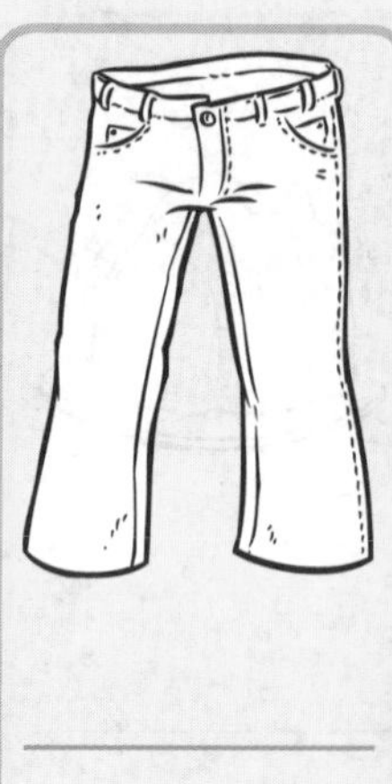

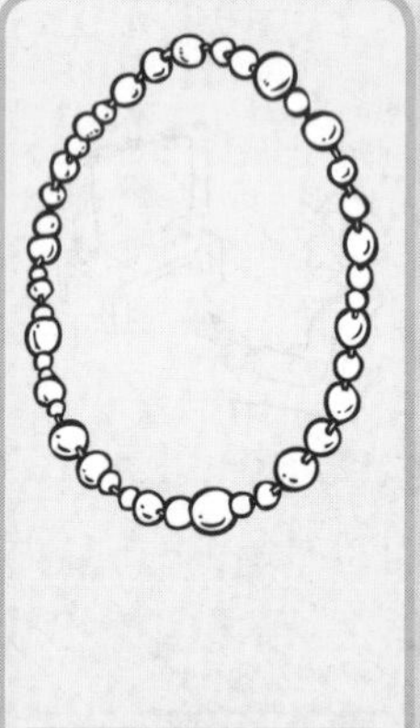

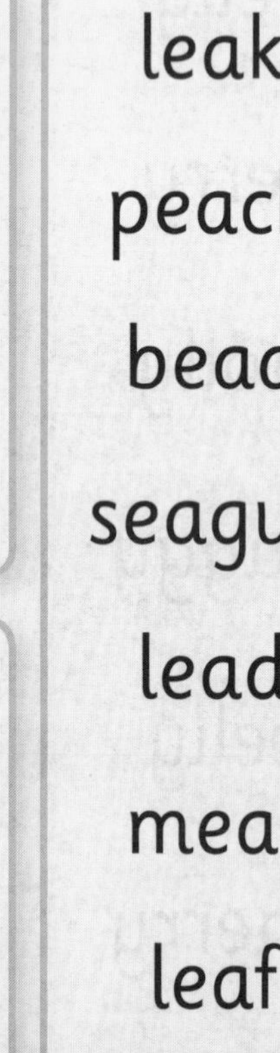

seagull

lead

meal

leaf

bleach

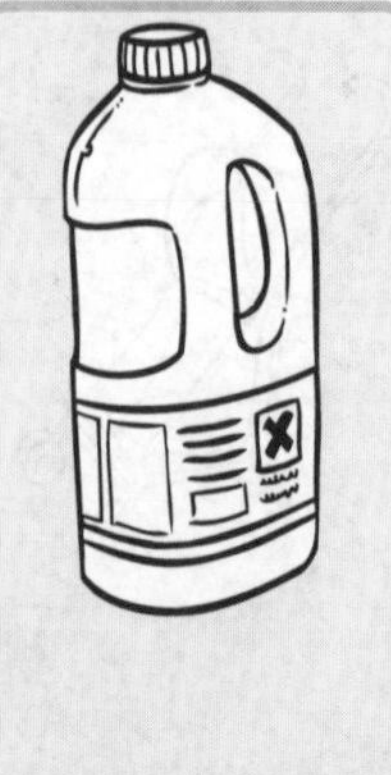

Objective: The child will be enabled to identify that the letters **ea** make the **/ee/** sound and read simple words with **ea**.

Read the words and circle the correct word.

pee
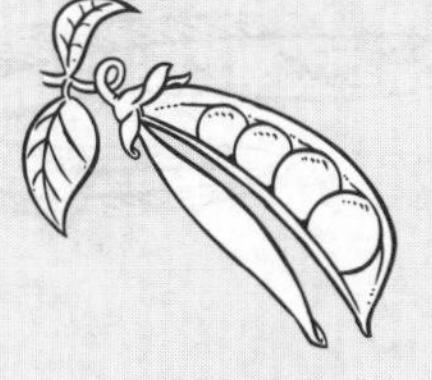
pea

beans

beens

jeep

jeap

sead

seed

wead

weed

beak

beek

leaf

leef

meet
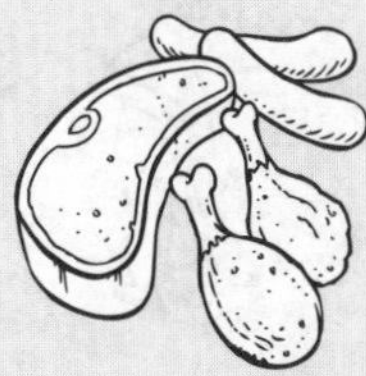
meat

eest

east

weep

weap

beap

beep

sheat
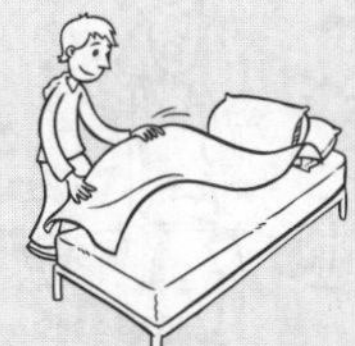
sheet

bleat

bleet

teepot

teapot

wheet

wheat

green

grean

Objective: The child will be enabled to identify if words with the **/ee/** sound are spelt with the letters **ee** or **ea**.

Write ee or ea for each word.

ee ea

s ___ ___

ee ea

r ___ d

ee ea

sl ___ ping

ee ea
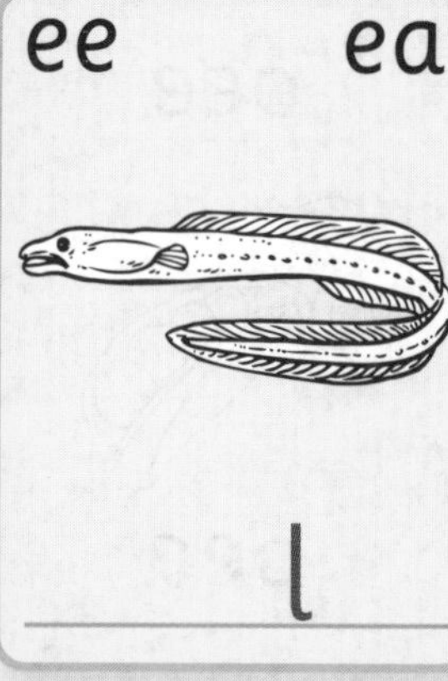
___ l

ee ea

sw ___ p

ee ea
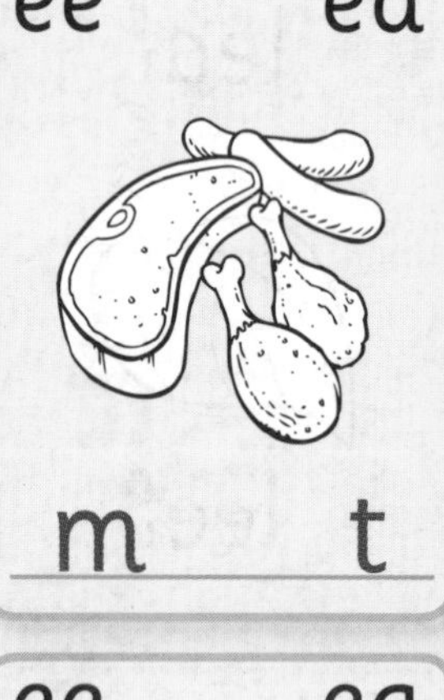
m ___ t

ee ea

w ___ k

ee ea

p ___ k

ee ea

w ___ k

ee ea

d ___ p

ee ea

sw ___ p

ee ea

gr ___ n

ee ea

cr ___ m

ee ea

str ___ m

ee ea

scr ___ m

ee ea

p ___ cock

Objective: The child will be enabled to identify if words with the **/ee/** sound are spelt with the letters **ee** or **ea**.

Read the sentences and fill in the correct word.

Do not ____________ at your present.
(peep, peak)

I like to drink ____________ drinks.
(fizzy, fishy)

When I was sick I felt very ____________.
(wheat, weak)

I put a quilt and ____________ on my bed.
(sheet, seed)

I planted ____________ seeds in the garden.
(puppy, poppy)

Do you want a cup of ____________ or ____________?
(coffee, cheese, tea)

We had to stop the ____________ because it had a flat ____________.
(weep, jeep, wheel)

I ate ____________ green ____________.
(sweets, three, seed)

When I go to bed and fall ____________, I ____________.
(dream, asleep, sweet)

Give the ____________ and the ____________ to the baby.
(dizzy, dolly, dummy)

Objective: The child will be enabled to complete cloze procedure activities based on vocabulary with the **/ee/** sound, spelt with the letters **ee**, **y** and **ea**.

Read the words and write the correct word under each picture.

brain	jail	tail	nail
hail	pigtail	nailbrush	stain

_______ _______ _______ _______

_______ _______ _______ _______

Read the sentences and fill in the correct word.

chain snail drain maid

A _______ cannot go very fast.

The _______ had to mop and sweep the floor.

Put the _______ and lock on the gate.

The _______ was blocked and Dad had to fix it.

Objective: The child will be enabled to identify that the letters **ai** make the **/ai/** sound and read simple words and sentences with **ai**.

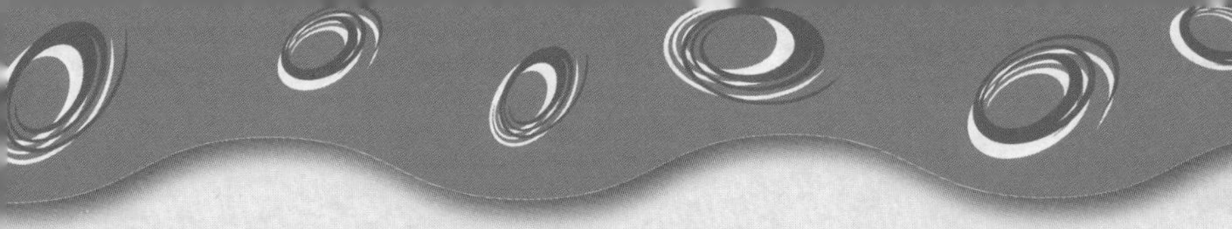

Read the words and write the correct word under each picture.

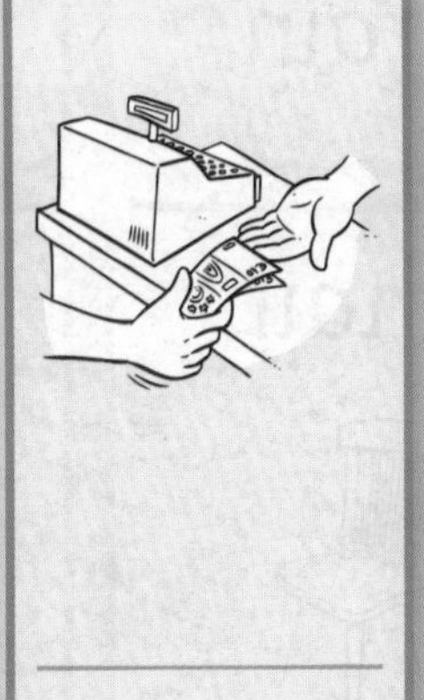

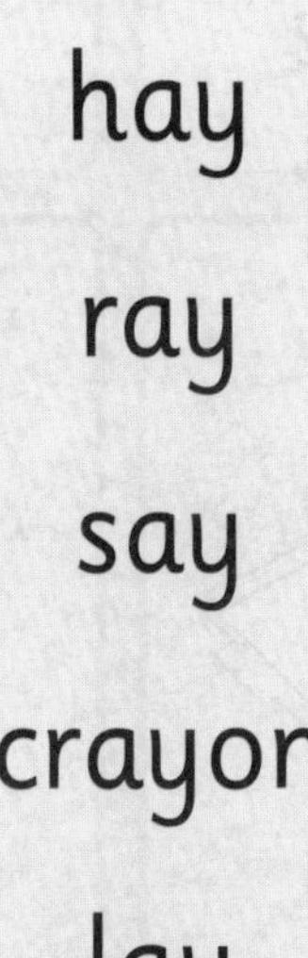

hay
ray
say
crayon
lay
pay
May
tray
clay
play
pray
runway

Objective: The child will be enabled to identify that the letters **ay** make the **/ai/** sound and read simple words with **ay**.

Read the words and circle the correct word.

play

plai

raik

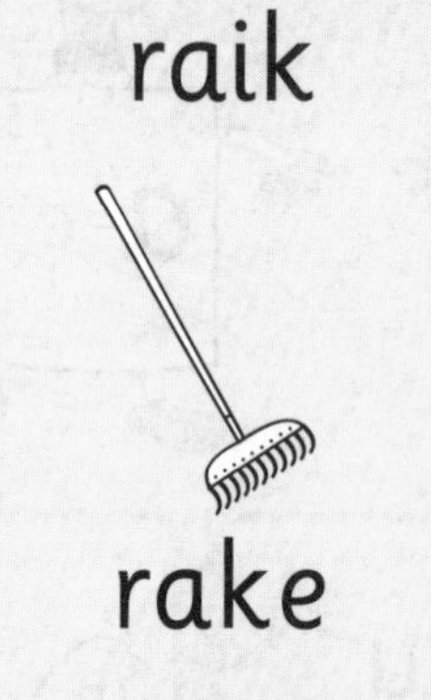

rake

trane

train

tape

taip

whale

whail

trai

tray

chair

chare

jayl

jail

craion

crayon

bake

bayk

case

cais

pai

pay

mermaid

mermade

runwai

runway

snail

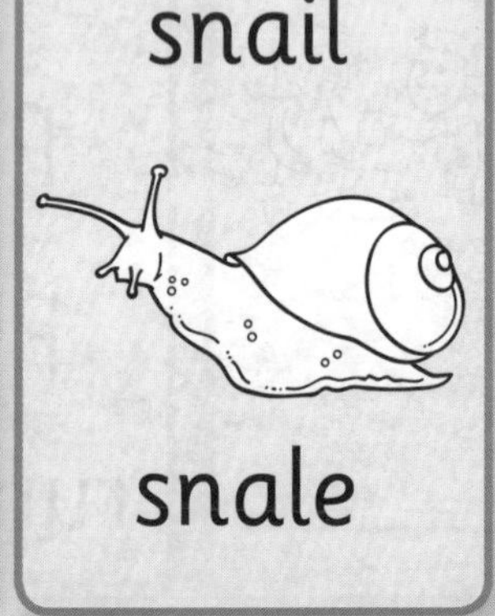

snale

plate

plait

Objective: The child will be enabled to identify if words with the **/ai/** sound are spelt with the letters **ai, Magic E** with a, or **ay**.

Write ai or ay for each word.

ai ay

holid

ai ay

pl

ai ay

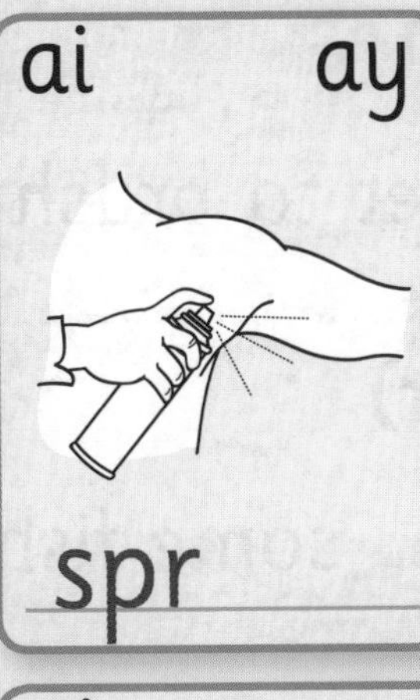

spr

ai ay

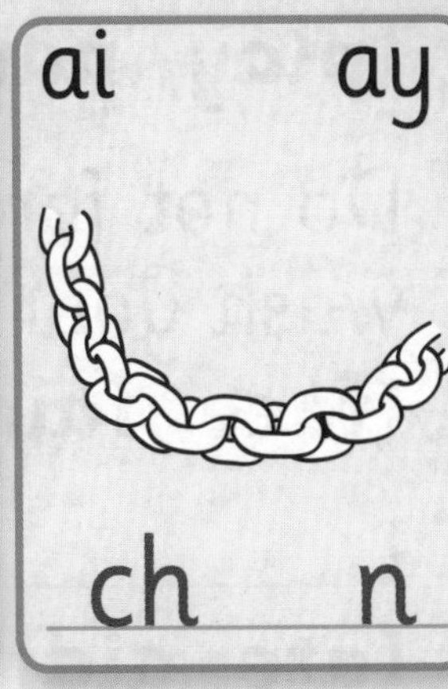

ch n

ai ay

n l

ai ay

s l

ai ay

tr n

ai ay

h

ai ay

pr

ai ay

r lw

ai ay

st n

ai ay

ch r

ai ay

pl pen

ai ay

s lor

ai ay

st rs

ai ay

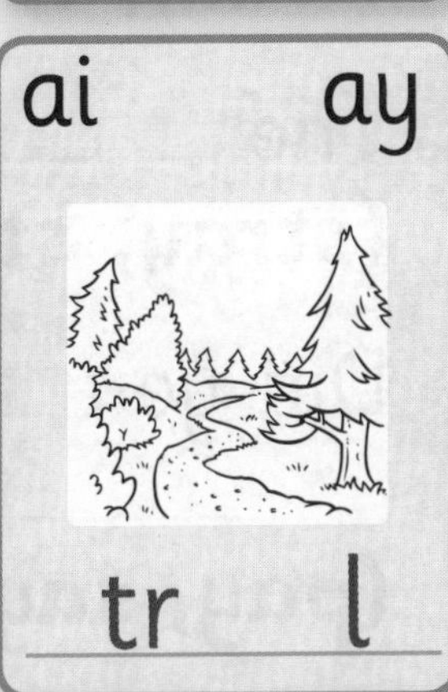

tr l

Objective: The child will be enabled to identify if words spelt with the **/ai/** sound are spelt with the letters **ai** or **ay**.

Read the sentences and fill in the correct word.

Tim must ____________ the milk bill.
(play, pay)

Do not forget to brush your hair and wash your ____________.
(face, faint)

I ____________ some fish and chips with ketchup.
(ate, aid)

I do not want to ____________ my test.
(fail, frail)

The man fed the pigs some ____________.
(hay, hail)

I had a ____________ muffin and glass of milk for a snack.
(ray, raisin)

Dad will ____________ the ____________ green.
(gate, paint, plain)

Do not be ________ for the six o'clock ________.
(train, laid, late)

The ________ cat had a cut on her ____________.
(stray, stain, tail)

Did you __________ you will __________ for the __________?
(pay, say, paint)

Objective: The child will be enabled to complete cloze procedure activities based on vocabulary with the /**ai**/ sound, spelt with the letters **ai**, **Magic E** with **a**, or **ay**.

Read the words and write the correct word under each picture.

pie	tie	die	cried
dried	spied	magpie	fried

Read the sentences and fill in the correct word.

tie cried died lies

I was upset when my pup ______.

That man likes to tell lots of ______.

I ______ when I bumped my leg.

Can you ______ the dog to the gate?

Objective: The child will be enabled to identify that the letters **ie** make the /ie/ sound and read simple words and sentences with **ie**.

Read the words and write the correct word under each picture.

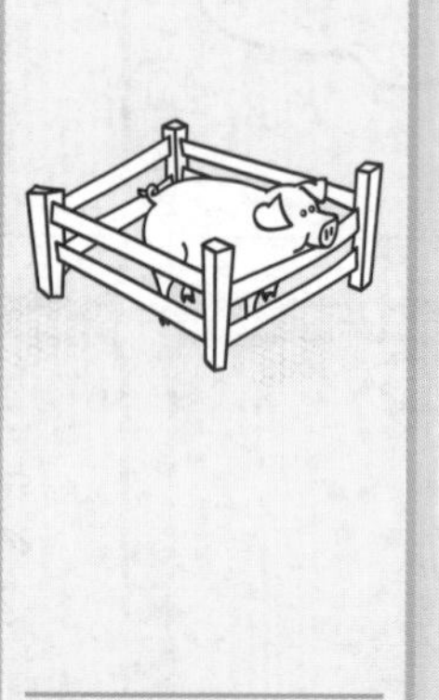

buy

fly

dry

cry

sky

fry

pigsty

my

sly

spy

why

shy

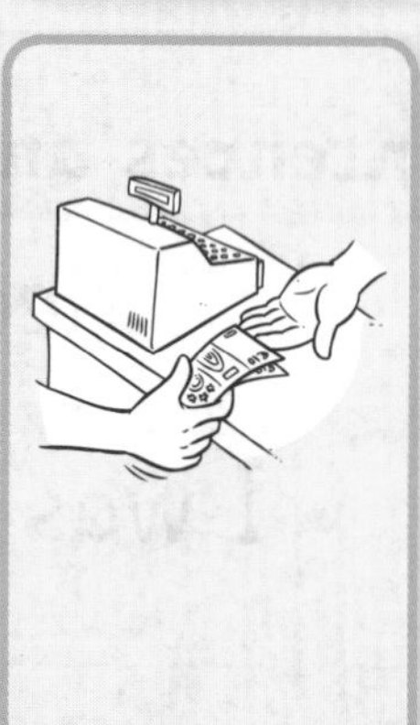

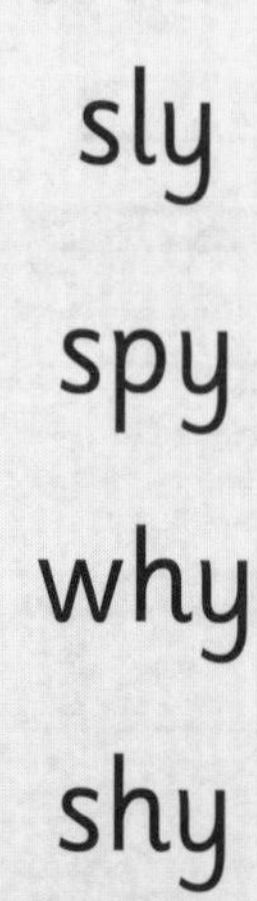

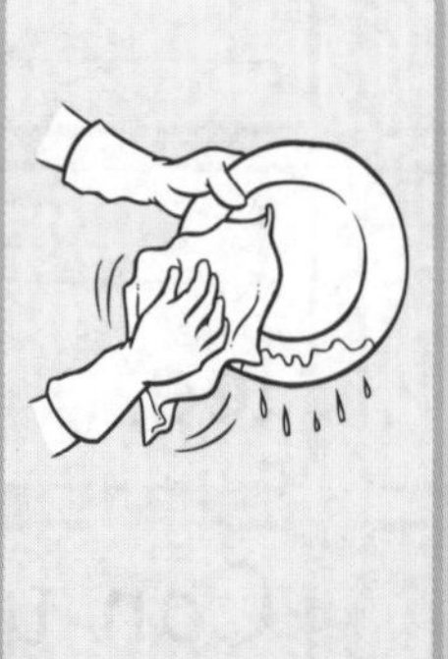

Objective: The child will be enabled to identify that the letter **y** at the end of a word can make the **/ie/** sound, and read simple words with **y** at the end.

Read the words and write the correct word under each picture.

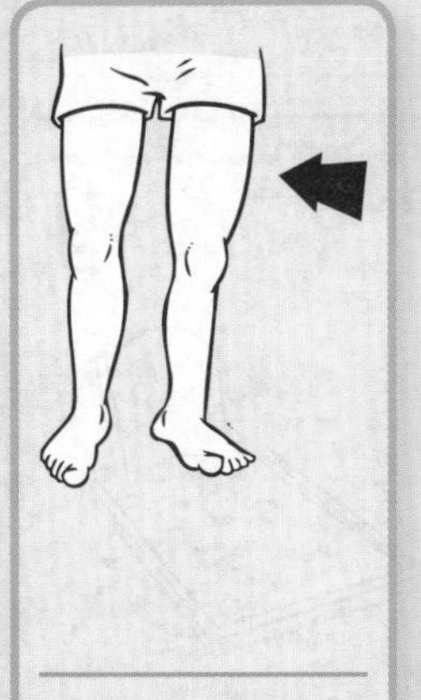

fight

light

flight

bright

fright

night

sigh

highchair

thigh

high

tights

tightrope

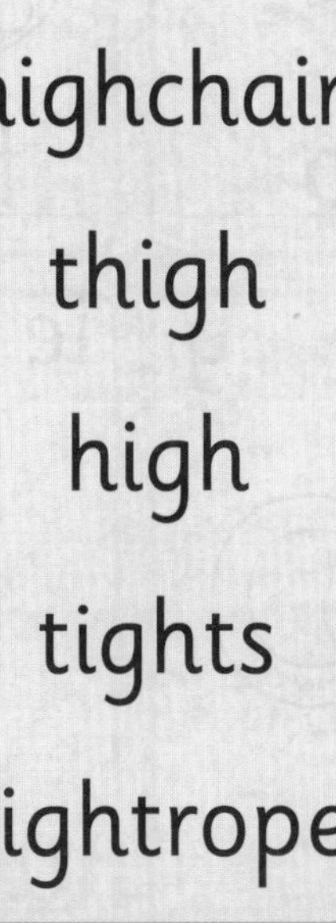

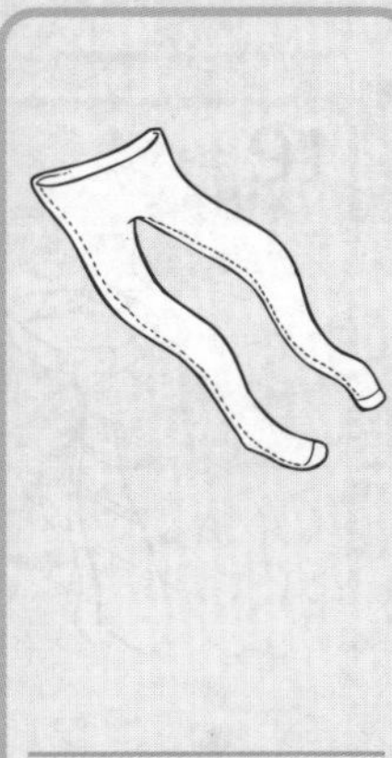

Objective: The child will be enabled to identify that the letters **igh** make the **/ie/** sound and read simple words with **igh**.

Write ie or y for each word.

ie y	ie y	ie y	ie y
p	wh	cr	m
bu	fl	gu	
l	magp	fr	d
t	dr	lullab	sk

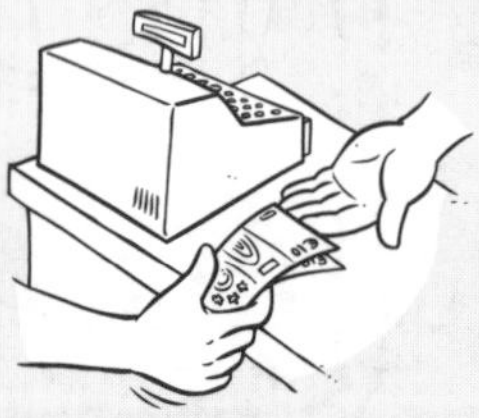

Objective: The child will be enabled to identify if words with the **/ie/** sound are spelt with the letters **ie** or **y**.

Read the words and circle the correct word.

pipe  piep	night  nite	light  lite	smighl  smile
fight  fite	spire 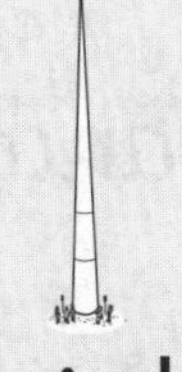 spighr	triek  trike	hive 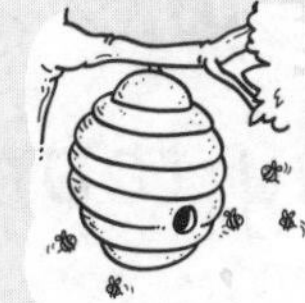 highv
briet  bright	fiev  five	spike  spighk	pie  pigh
fright  friet	sie  sigh	dighv  dive	drive  driev

Objective: The child will be enabled to identify if words with the /ie/ sound are spelt with the letters **ie, Magic E** with **i**, or **igh**.

Read the sentences and fill in the correct word.

My grandad likes to smoke his ____________.
(pipe, pies)

____________ your boots so you do not trip.
(tie, tries)

Can you ____________ the dishes?
(dry, die)

The boy hid behind his dad as he was ________.
(sigh, shy)

My top shrunk in the wash and was a bit ____________.
(thigh, tight)

It is very rude to ____________.
(sight, sigh)

I had a ________ for ________ lunch.
(fry, my)

Gran had a big ____________ last ____________.
(night, might, fright)

That small boy can ____________ his ____________.
(right, trike, ride)

The ____________ went high up into the ____________.
(kite, sky, high)

Objective: The child will be enabled to complete cloze procedure activities based on vocabulary with the **/ie/** sound spelt with the letters **ie**, **y** and **igh**.

Read the words and write the correct word under each picture.

boat	float	foal	moat
loaf	roast	toad	waistcoat

______

______

______

______

______

______

______

______

Read the sentences and fill in the correct word.

oats cloak road coast

The witch had a wand, a broom and a ______.

There are lots of cliffs beside the ______.

I like to eat ______ and toast for breakfast.

The man can drive a crane on the ______.

Objective: The child will be enabled to identify that the letters **oa** make the **/oa/** sound and read simple words and sentences with **oa**.

Read the words and write the correct word under each picture.

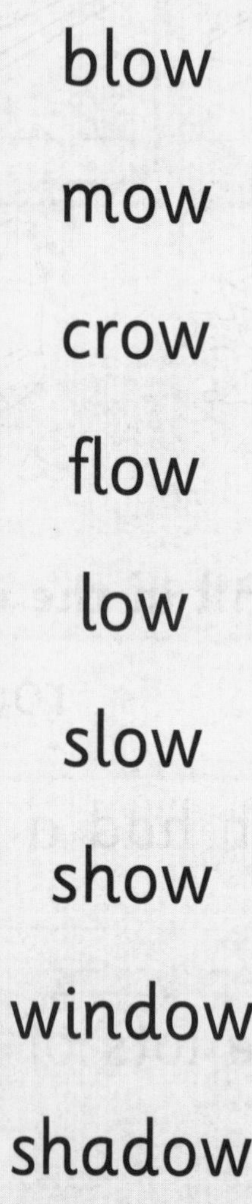

blow

mow

crow

flow

low

slow

show

window

shadow

follow

tow

snowball

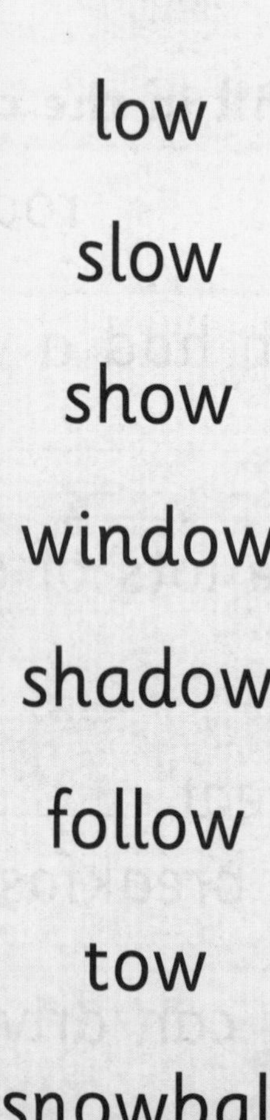

Objective: The child will be enabled to identify that the letters **ow** make the **/oa/** sound and read simple words with **ow**.

Read the words and circle the correct word.

tow	blow	coat	gowt

toa	bloa	cowt	goat
crow	fowm	snow	soap

croa	foam	snoa	sowp
oak	toast	row	pilloa
			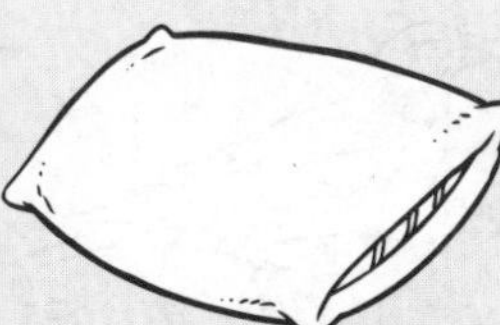
owk	towst	roa	pillow
elbow	blowt	arroa	sloa
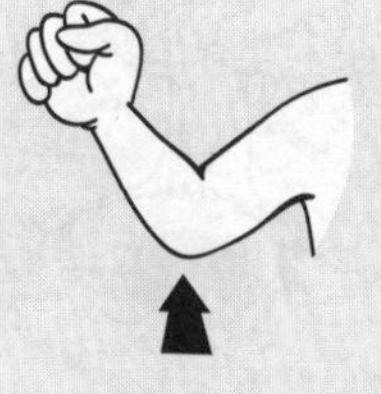			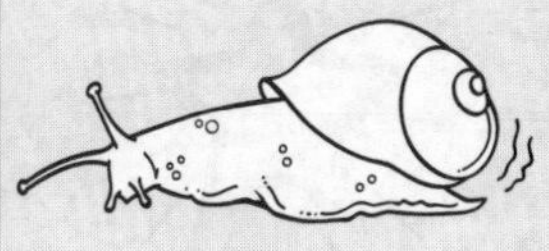
elboa	bloat	arrow	slow

Objective: The child will be enabled to identify if words with the **/oa/** sound are spelt with the letters **oa** or **ow**.

Write oa or ow for each word.

oa ow  s ___	oa ow  b ___	oa ow  yell ___	oa ow  b ___ t
oa ow  r ___ st	oa ow  cl ___ k	oa ow  gr ___	oa ow  s ___ p
oa ow  cr ___	oa ow  sn ___ flake	oa ow  br ___ ch	oa ow  cl ___ kroom
oa ow  gl ___	oa ow 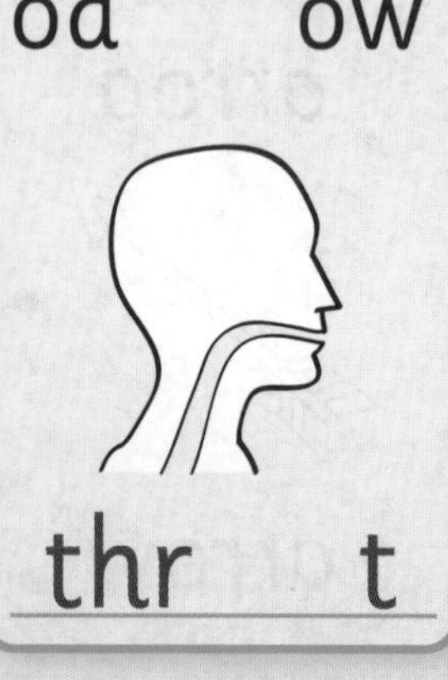 thr ___ t	oa ow  st ___ t	oa ow 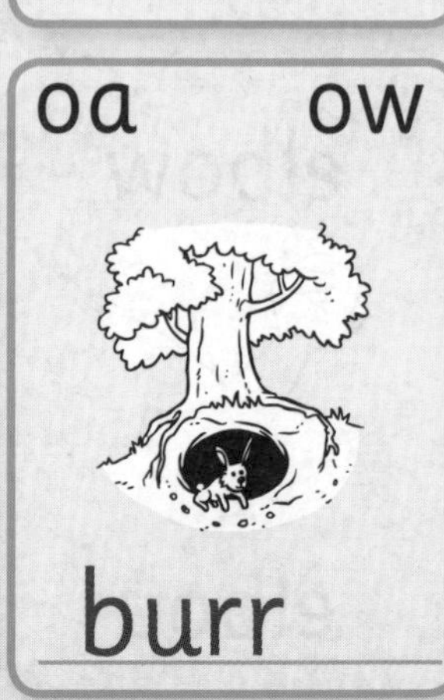 burr ___

Objective: The child will be enabled to identify if words with the **/oa/** sound are spelt with the letters **oa** or **ow**.

Read the sentences and fill in the correct word.

My dad __________ a big, red car.
(oats, owns)

We put a hat on the __________.
(snowman, soap)

My dad likes to soak me with the __________.
(hope, home, hose)

Did you see that big, fat __________ jump in the pond?
(throat, toad)

I like to plant seeds in a pot and watch them __________.
(grow, glow)

Dad uses shaving __________ when he shaves.
(foal, foam)

Gran put a __________ __________ in my hair.
(blow, yellow, bow)

I can __________ the __________.
(boat, row, road)

There is a hole in the __________ of my __________.
(elbow, coast, coat)

I saw a __________ on the side of the __________.
(roast, road, crow)

Objective: The child will be enabled to complete cloze procedure activities based on vocabulary with the **/oa/** sound spelt with the letters **oa**, **Magic E** with **o** and **ow**.

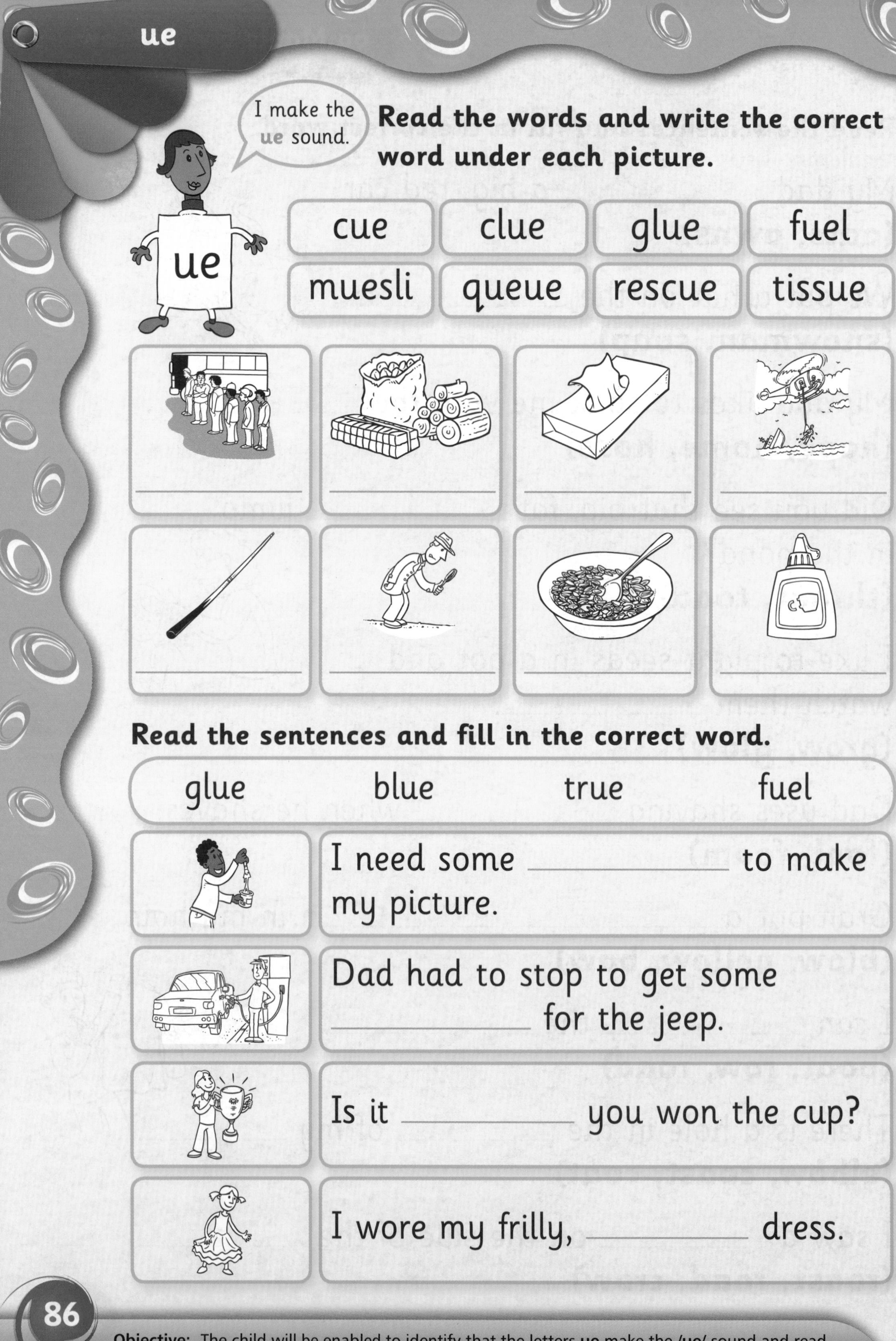

Read the words and write the correct word under each picture.

cue	clue	glue	fuel
muesli	queue	rescue	tissue

Read the sentences and fill in the correct word.

glue   blue   true   fuel

I need some ____________ to make my picture.

Dad had to stop to get some ____________ for the jeep.

Is it ____________ you won the cup?

I wore my frilly, ____________ dress.

Objective: The child will be enabled to identify that the letters **ue** make the **/ue/** sound and read simple words and sentences with **ue**.

Read the words and write the correct word under each picture.

We all make the **ue** sound.

pew
new
stew
blew
chew
crew
flew
drew
grew
jewel
newt
dew

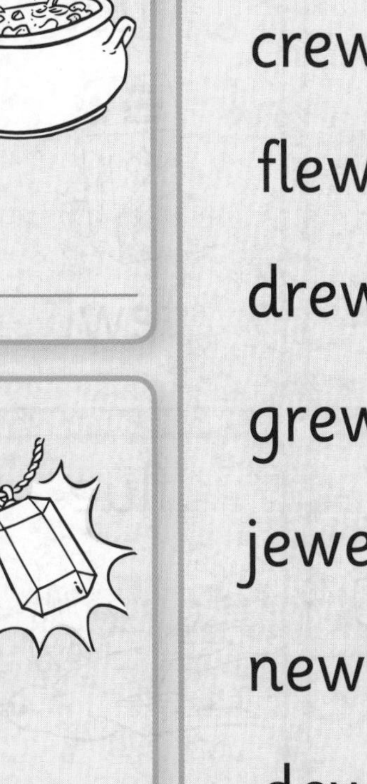

Objective: The child will be enabled to identify that the letters **ew** make the **/ue/** sound and read simple words with **ew**.

Read the words and circle the correct word.

pew  pue	stew  steu	glew  glue	clue  clew
blue what colour are these?  blew	blue  blew	chue  chew	drew  drue
cue 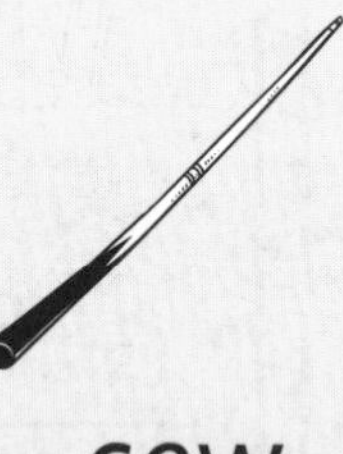 cew	juel  jewel	fuel 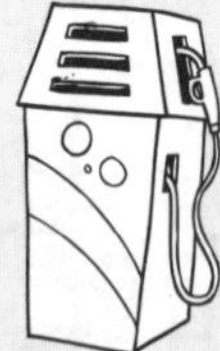 fewl	muesli  mewsli
queue  quew	tissue  tissew	flue  flew	grew  grue

Objective: The child will be enabled to identify if words with the **/ue/** sound are spelt with the letters **ue** or ew.

Write ue or ew for each word.

ue ew  n____	ue ew  cr____	ue ew 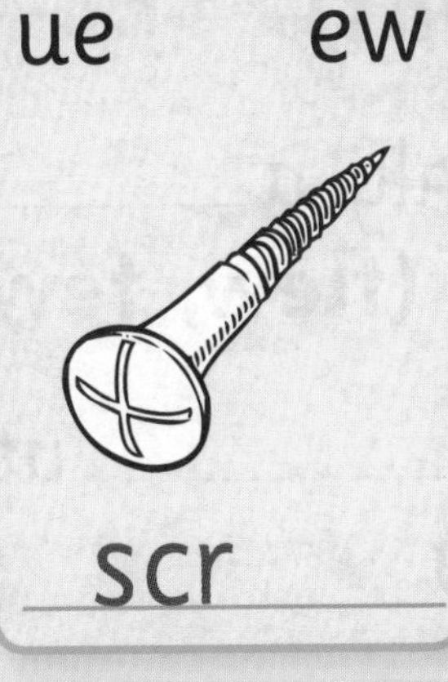 scr____	ue ew  f____l
ue ew  tiss____	ue ew  n____s	ue ew  q____	ue ew  thr____
ue ew  n____t	ue ew  resc____	ue ew  d____	ue ew  st____
ue ew  j____el	ue ew  ch____y	ue ew  f____	ue ew  gl____

Objective: The child will be enabled to identify if words with the **/ue/** sound are spelt with the letters **ue** or **ew**.

Read the sentences and fill in the correct word.

I ____________ the ball for Beth to catch it.
(threw, owns)

There are only a ____________ boys in my class. **(flew, few)**

The robin ____________ up into the nest in the tree.
(fuel, flew)

We got a ____________ big, black, flashy car.
(new, blue)

I ____________ a sketch of Dad in my sketchpad.
(drew, dew)

I love to ____________ toffees but they stick to my teeth.
(crew, chew)

The man could not swim and Dad had to ____________ him.
(rescue, queue)

I rubbed the ____________ with a ____________.
(jewel, tissue, true)

Is it true you got a ____________, ____________ jeep?
(news, blue, new)

My pet kitten is very ____________.
(cube, cute, clue)

Objective: The child will be enabled to complete cloze procedure activities based on vocabulary with the **/ue/** sound, spelt with the letters **ue, Magic E** with **u** and **ew**.

Read the words and write the correct word under each picture.

boil	coil	spoilt	doily
noise	oil	soil	point

  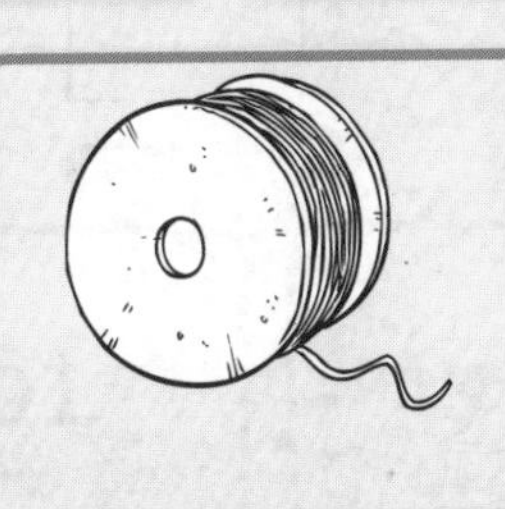 

  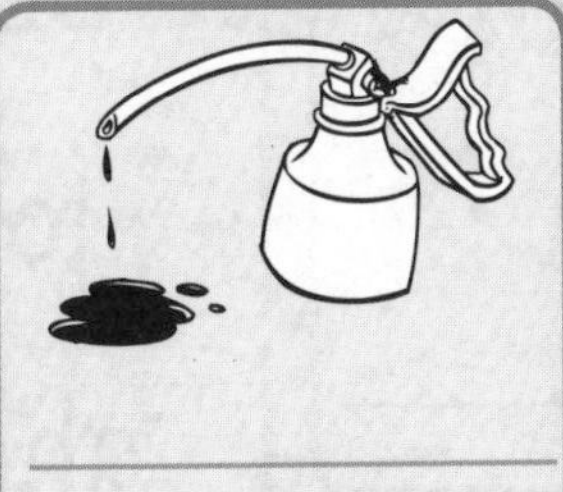 

Read the sentences and fill in the correct word.

coins   poison   tinfoil   join

We had to ____________ the dots in class.

My grandad likes to collect ____________.

The ____________ will kill the rats.

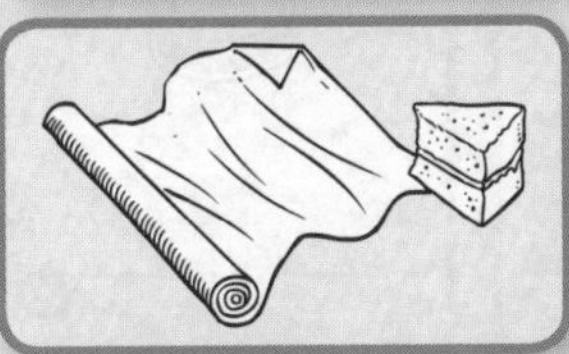

Mum put the cake in some ____________.

Objective: The child will be enabled to identify that the letters **oi** make the **/oi/** sound and read simple words and sentences with **oi**.

Read the words and write the correct word under each picture.

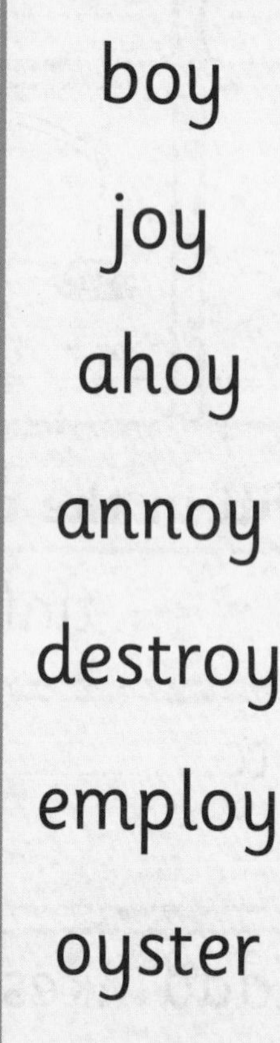

toy
boy
joy
ahoy
annoy
destroy
employ
oyster
royal
enjoy
pageboy
soya

Objective: The child will be enabled to identify that the letters **oy** make the **/oi/** sound and read simple words with **oy**.

Read the words and circle the correct word.

boil  boyl	boy  boi	ahoi  ahoy	oil  oyl
soil  soyl	poynt  point	coins  coyns	joi  joy
spoylt  spoilt	annoy  annoy	destroi  destroy	pageboy  pageboi
roial  royal	enjoi  enjoy	coil 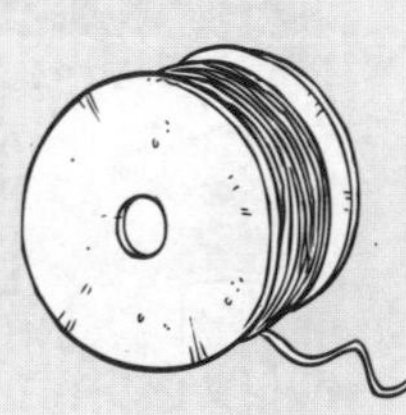 coyl	foyl  foil

Objective: The child will be enabled to identify if words with the **/oi/** sound are spelt with the letters **oi** or **oy**.

Write oi or oy for each word.

Objective: The child will be enabled to identify if words with the **/oi/** sound are spelt with the letters **oi** or **oy**.

Read the sentences and fill in the correct word.

__________ the milk in the pot on the stove.
(boil, boy)

That rude kid is __________.
(spoil, spoilt)

I was full of __________ when I won the prize.
(joy, enjoy)

The __________ gave the groom the rings.
(boy, pageboy)

Dad has a __________ of wire in the shed.
(coil, coin)

Would you like to __________ us for lunch?
(joy, join)

That film was not very good, I did not __________ it at all.
(employ, enjoy)

If you __________ the milk too much you will __________ it.
(soil, boil, spoil)

Dad put the __________ in __________.
(toilet, oysters, tinfoil)

Pat will __________ a man to fix the __________.
(toilet, poison, employ)

Objective: The child will be enabled to complete cloze procedure activities based on vocabulary with the /oi/ sound spelt with the letters oi and oy.

I make the **ou** sound.

ou

Read the words and write the correct word under each picture.

hound	mouse	hour	snout
slouch	sour	spout	south

N E S W

______ ______ ______ ______

______ ______ ______ ______

Read the sentences and fill in the correct word.

proud nouns count ouch

1234

I can ____________ to one hundred.

I was very ____________ when I did well in my test.

____________, that was sore.

cow
dog
girl
rat
house
foot
bird

We had to write a list of ____________ in our copy books.

Objective: The child will be enabled to identify that the letters **ou** make the **/ou/** sound and read simple words and sentences with **ou**.

Read the words and write the correct word under each picture.

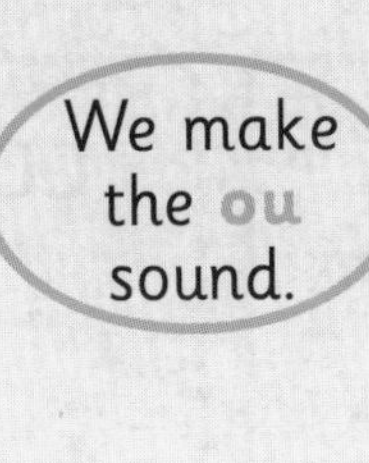

howl

gown

frown

growl

brow

down

crowd

cow

clown

crown

owl

brown

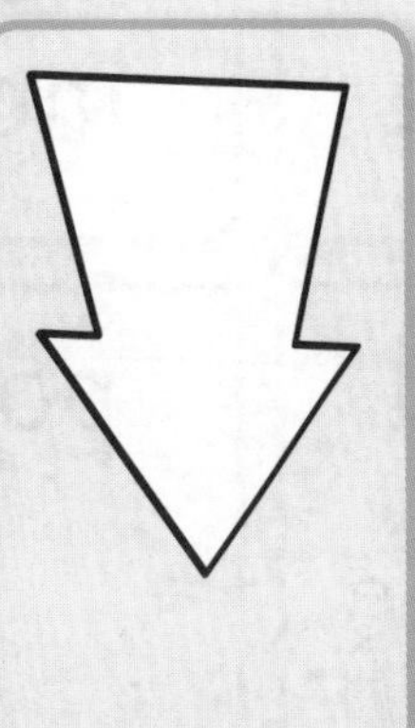

Objective: The child will be enabled to identify that the letters **ow** make the **/ou/** sound and read simple words with **ow**.

Read the words and circle the correct word.

howse

house

mouth
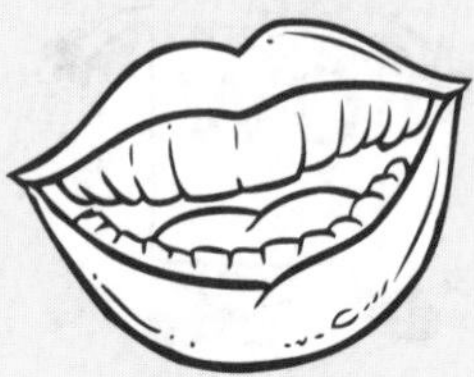
mowth

out

owt

couboy

cowboy

crowd

croud

powch

pouch

couch

cowch

owl

oul

round

rownd

playgrownd

playground

crown

croun

broun

brown

grownd

ground

lowd

loud

vowel

vouel

gown

goun

Objective: The child will be enabled to identify if words with the **/ou/** sound are spelt with the letters **ou** or **ow**.

Write ou or ow for each word.

ou ow

bl se

ou ow

t el

ou ow

cl d

ou ow

c ch

ou ow

tr el

ou ow

v el

ou ow

t n

ou ow

eyebr

ou ow

sh t

ou ow

fl r

ou ow

c ard

ou ow

fr n

ou ow

sc t

ou ow

c

ou ow

s r

ou ow

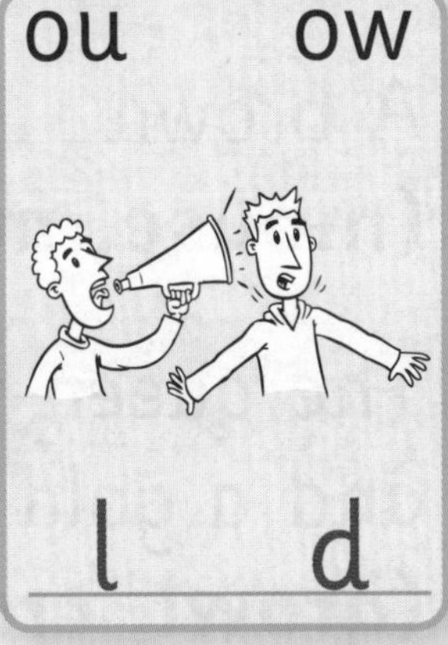

l d

Objective: The child will be enabled to identify if words with the **/ou/** sound are spelt with the letters **ou** or **ow**.

Read the sentences and fill in the correct word.

Can you ____________ to ten?
(couch, count)

The sly fox has a big ____________.
(spout, snout)

The kids had good fun with the ____________.
(clown, cloud)

Dad likes to drink a glass of beer or ____________.
(shout, stout)

I was very ____________ when I won the prize.
(proud, pouch)

Can you get me a fresh ____________ to dry myself?
(trowel, towel)

The spoilt kid likes to ____________ and ____________.
(out, pout, frown)

The ____________ made the dog give a ____________.
(bow, clown, vowel)

A brown ____________ hid in our ____________.
(mouse, mouth, couch)

The queen wore a long ____________
and a gold ____________.
(growl, crown, gown)

Objective: The child will be enabled to complete cloze procedure activities based on vocabulary with the **/ou/** sound spelt with the letters **ou** or **ow**.

Read the words and write the correct word under each picture.

fork	chord	acorn	forty
popcorn	stork	thorn	passport

_____

_____

_____

_____

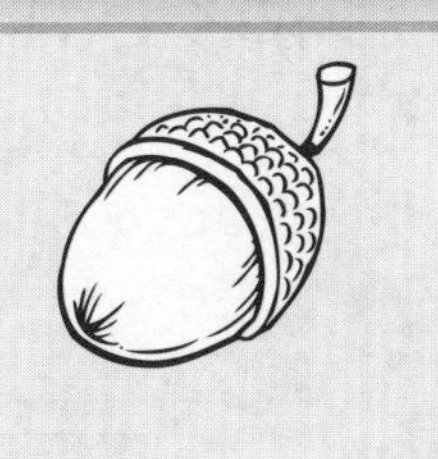
_____

_____

_____

_____

Read the sentences and fill in the correct word.

popcorn forget torch horse

Do not __________ to do your homework tonight.

I had a big box of __________ when we watched a film.

The man put the __________ in the shed when it began to rain.

I brought a sleeping bag and __________ when we went camping.

Objective: The child will be enabled to identify that the letters **or** make the **/or/** sound and read simple words and sentences with **or**.

Read the words and write the correct word under each picture.

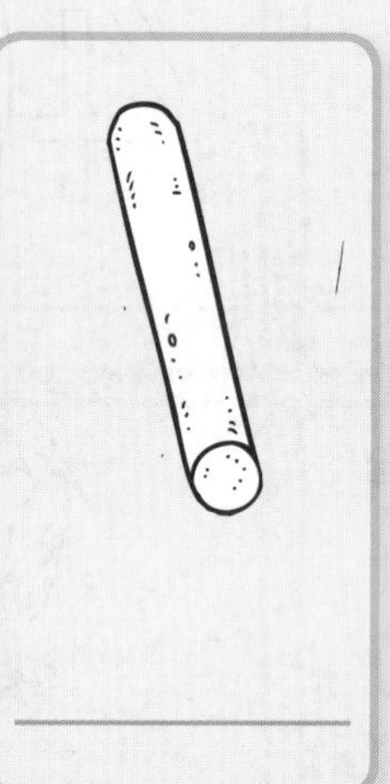

fall

wall

ball

all

small

walk

talk

stalk

chalk

catwalk

tall

sleepwalk

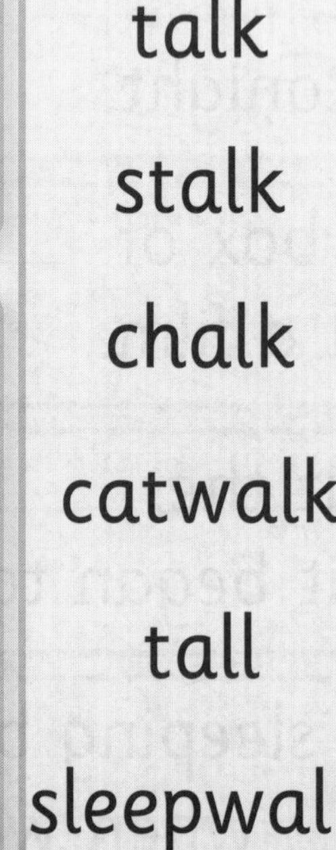

Objective: The child will be enabled to identify that the letters **al** make the **/aw/** sound and read simple words with **al**.

Read the words and write the correct word under each picture.

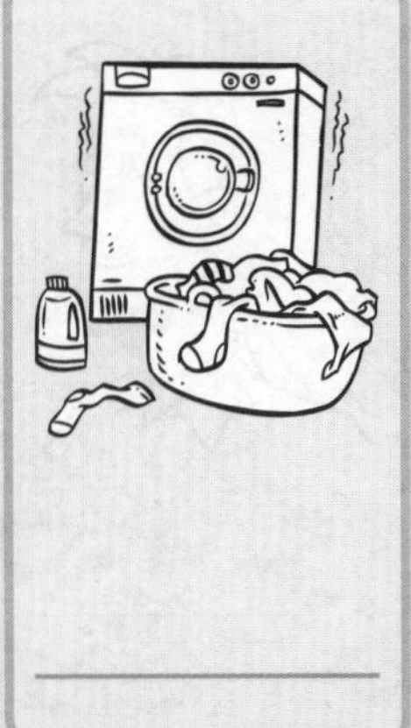

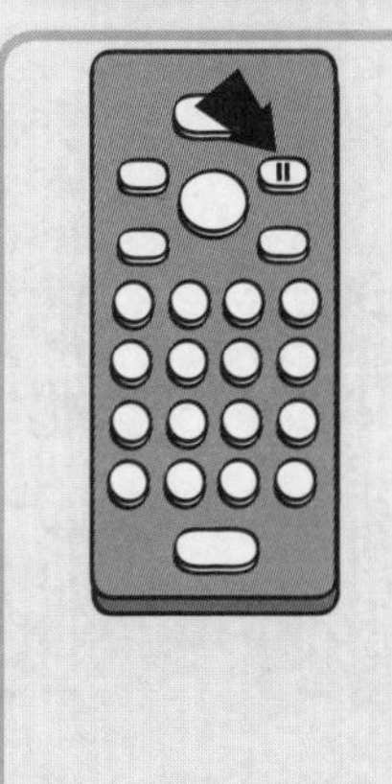

Objective: The child will be enabled to identify that the letters **au** make the **/aw/** sound and read simple words with **au**.

Read the words and write the correct word under each picture.

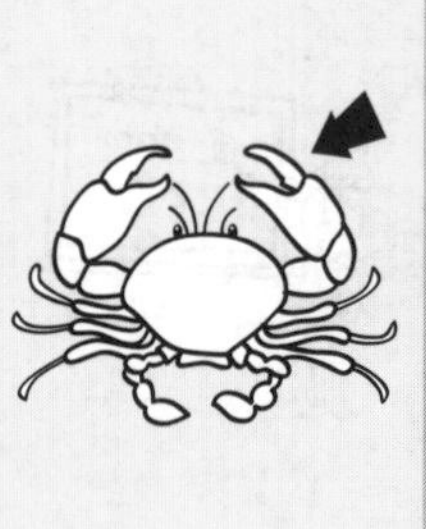
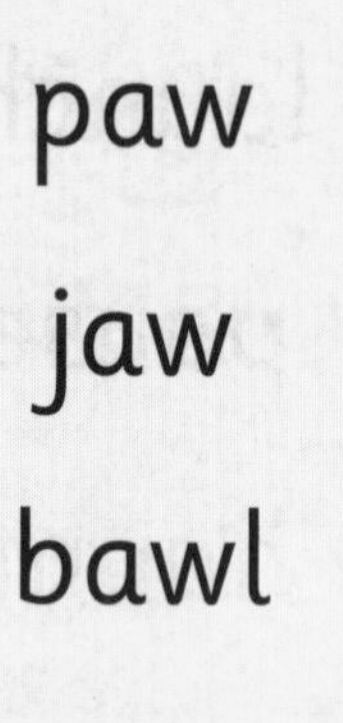

paw
jaw
bawl
dawn
claw
hawk
draw
straw
yawn
prawn
seesaw
saw

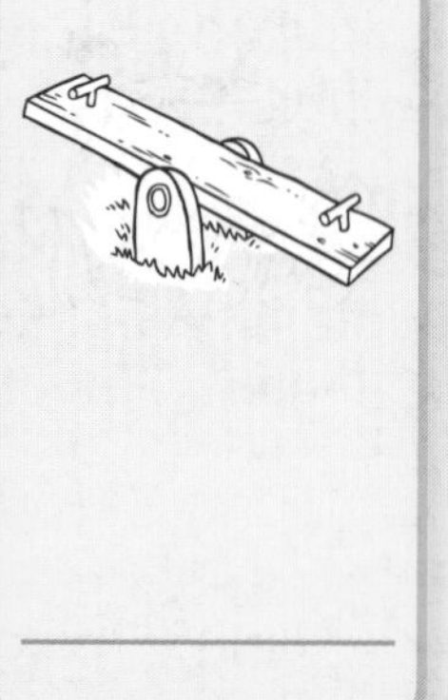
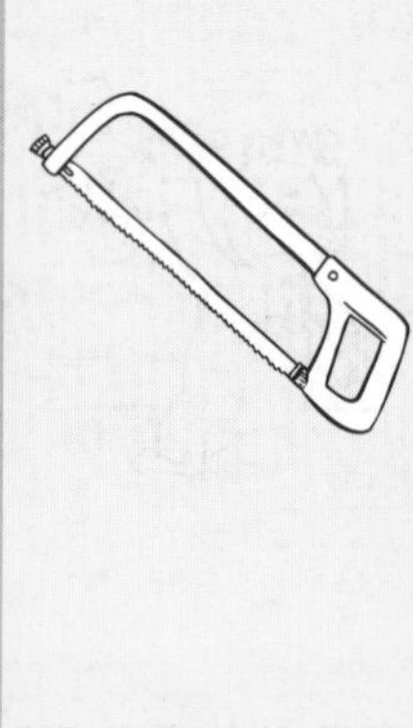

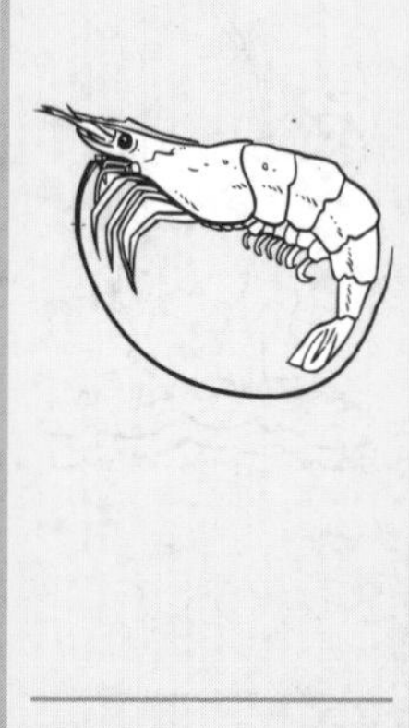
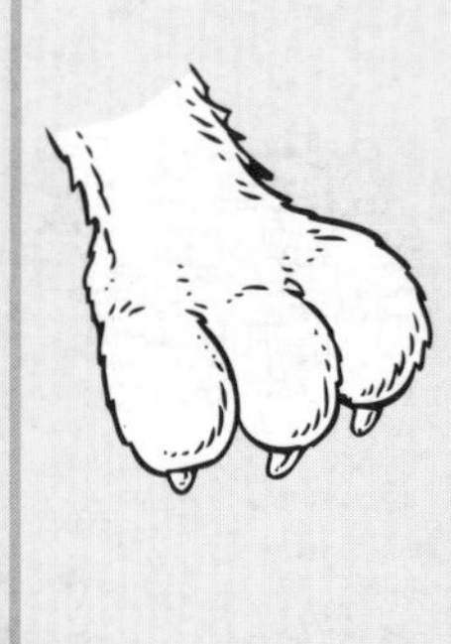

Objective: The child will be enabled to identify that the letters **aw** make the **/aw/** sound and read simple words with **aw**.

Read the sentences and fill in the correct word.

My favourite ______________ is football.
(short, sport)

We went on a long ______________ up the hill.
(walk, sleepwalk)

I had a can of coke and a packet of ______________ for a snack.
(porch, popcorn)

Our car made lots of noise when the ______________ was broken.
(flaw, exhaust)

We love to go to the ______________ to see the planes taking off.
(airport, heliport)

When we do our work in class we are not to ______.
(talk, thorn)

The man gave the __________ some __________ to eat.
(straw, shawl, horse)

The __________ boy hid the __________ on Dad.
(naughty, saw, snort)

Do not ______________ to bring the ______________ when we go camping.
(torn, torch, forget)

The boy began to ______________ when he fell off the ______________.
(bawl, born, seesaw)

Objective: The child will be enabled to complete cloze procedure activities based on vocabulary with the **/or/** sound spelt with the letters **or** and with the **/aw/** sound spelt with the letters **al**, **au** and **aw**.

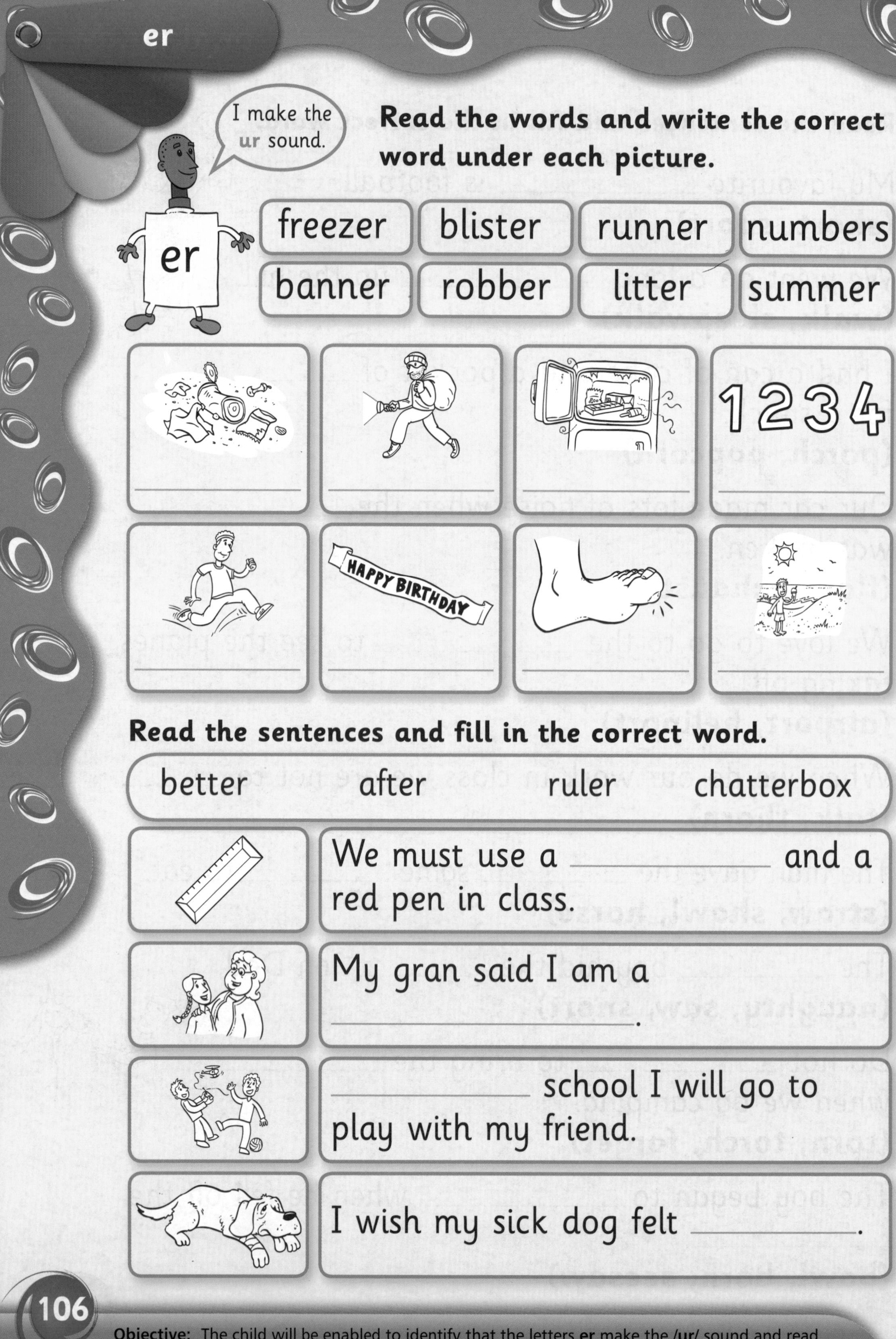

Read the words and write the correct word under each picture.

freezer	blister	runner	numbers
banner	robber	litter	summer

Read the sentences and fill in the correct word.

better after ruler chatterbox

We must use a __________ and a red pen in class.

My gran said I am a __________.

__________ school I will go to play with my friend.

I wish my sick dog felt __________.

Objective: The child will be enabled to identify that the letters **er** make the **/ur/** sound and read simple words with **er**.

Read the words and write the correct word under each picture.

sir

girl

chirp

skirt

swirl

squirt

squirm

bird

thirst

smirk

whirlwind

third

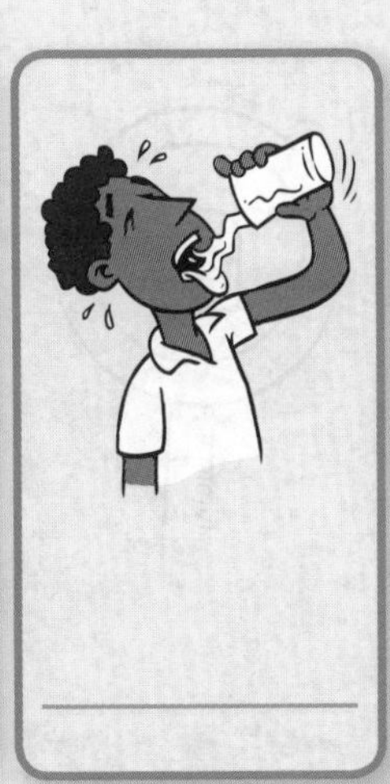

Objective: The child will be enabled to identify that the letters **ir** make the **/ur/** sound and read simple words with **ir**.

Read the words and write the correct word under each picture.

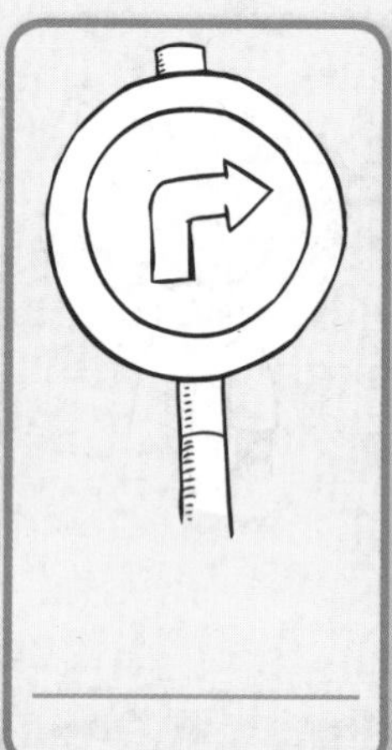

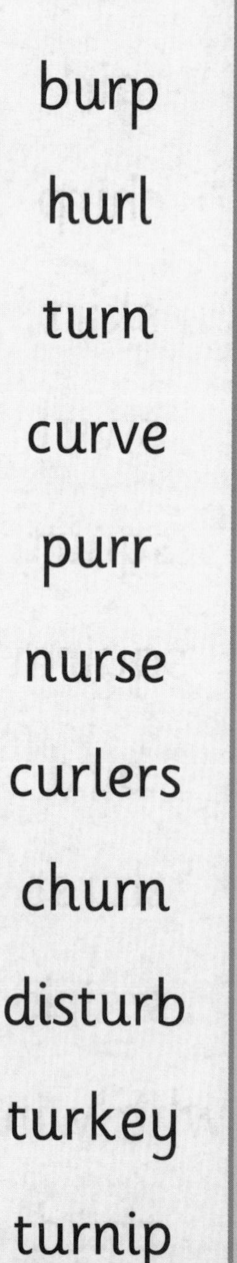

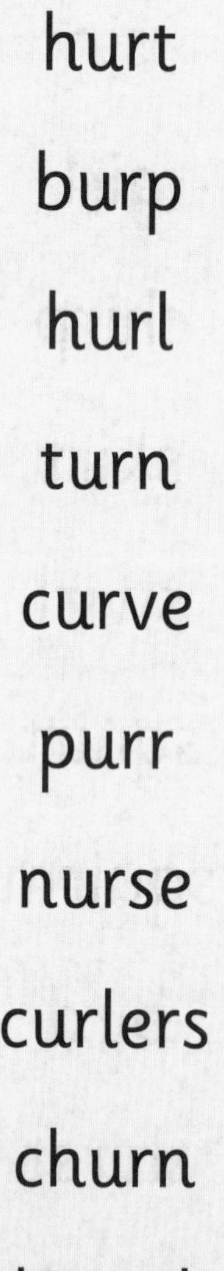

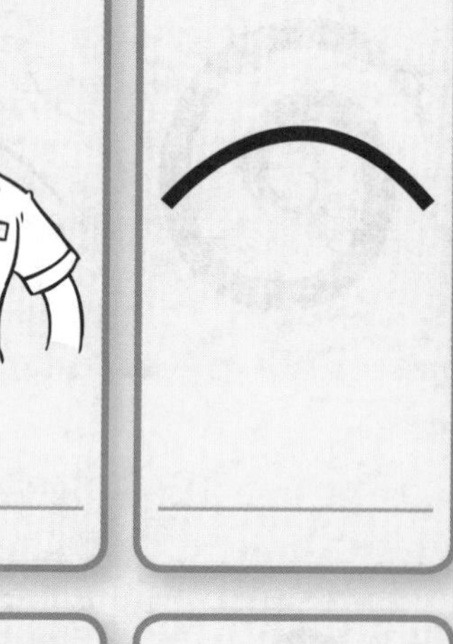

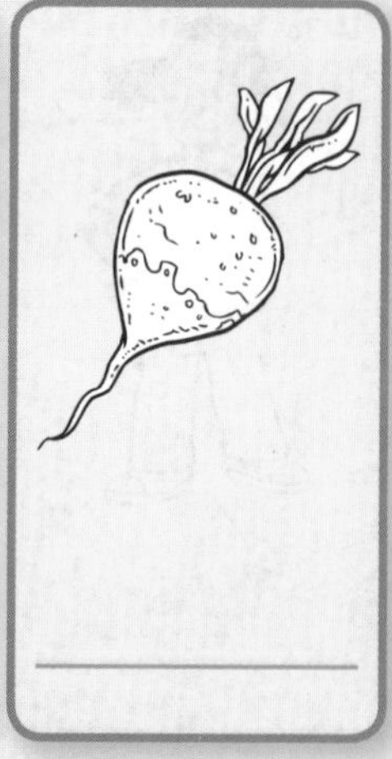

Objective: The child will be enabled to identify that the letters **ur** make the **/ur/** sound and read simple words with **ur**.

Read the words and circle the correct word.

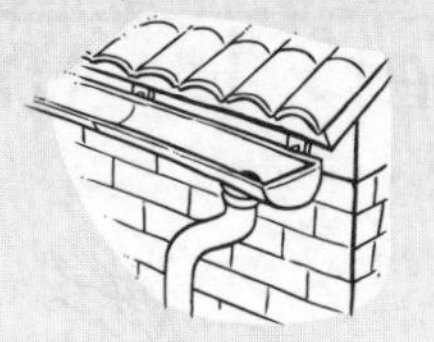

gutter
guttur
guttir

robbir
robbur
robber

virb
verb
vurb

burd
bird
berd

gurl
gerl
girl

burst
birst
berst

shurt
shert
shirt

church
cherch
chirch

lettir
lettur
letter

surf
serf
sirf

burger
burgur
burger

skurt
skirt
skert

therd
third
thurd

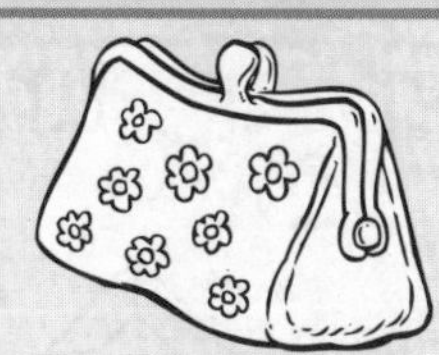

perse
pirse
purse

stir
stur
ster

cerly
cirly
curly

Objective: The child will be enabled to identify if words with the **/ur/** sound are spelt with the letters **er**, **ir** or **ur**.

Write er, ir or ur for each word.

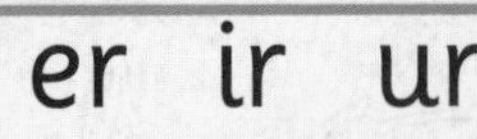

er ir ur

tig

er ir ur

13

th teen

er ir ur

show

er ir ur

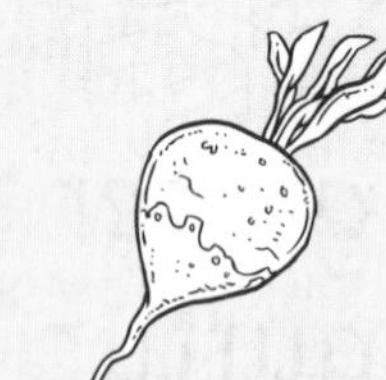

t nip

er ir ur

d t

er ir ur

b n

er ir ur

h d

er ir ur

t tle

er ir ur

lobst

er ir ur

div

er ir ur

sm k

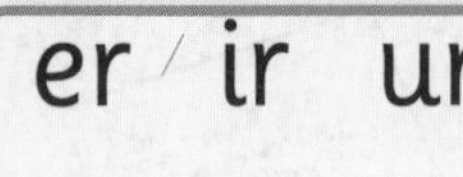

er ir ur

b ger

er ir ur

b th

er ir ur

sunb n

er ir ur

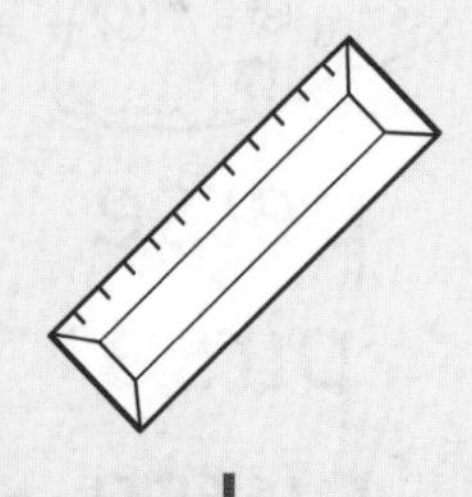

rul

er ir ur

scoot

Objective: The child will be enabled to identify if words with the **/ur/** sound are spelt with the letters **er**, **ir**, or **ur**.

Read the sentences and fill in the correct word.

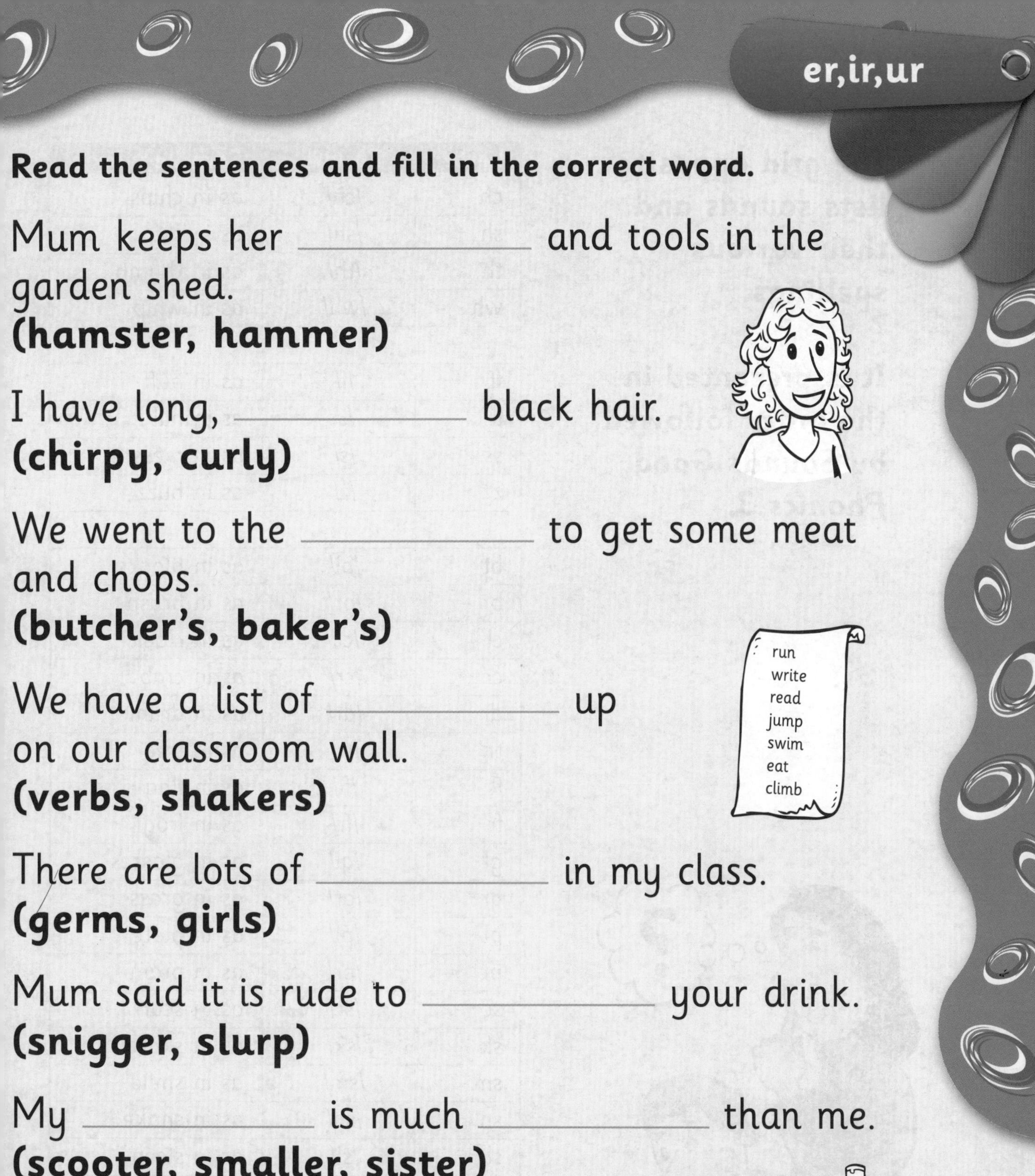

Mum keeps her ____________ and tools in the garden shed.
(hamster, hammer)

I have long, ____________ black hair.
(chirpy, curly)

We went to the ____________ to get some meat and chops.
(butcher's, baker's)

We have a list of ____________ up on our classroom wall.
(verbs, shakers)

There are lots of ____________ in my class.
(germs, girls)

Mum said it is rude to ____________ your drink.
(snigger, slurp)

My ____________ is much ____________ than me.
(scooter, smaller, sister)

My ____________ was ____________ after the football match.
(dirty, digger, jersey)

I had a ____________ and chips with ketchup for my ____________.
(burger, dinner, dessert)

Objective: The child will be enabled to complete cloze procedure activities based on vocabulary with the **/ur/** sound spelt with the letters **er**, **ir** and **ur**.

The grid opposite lists sounds and their various spellings.

It is presented in the order followed by *Sounds Good Phonics 3*.

Letter	Sound	Sample words
ch	/ch/	as in chips
sh	/sh/	as in ship
th	/th/	as in thumb
wh	/wh/	as in whip
ff	/f/	as in huff
ll	/l/	as in hill
ss	/s/	as in mess
zz	/z/	as in buzz
bl	/bl/	as in blocks
br	/br/	as in brush
cl	/cl/	as in clock
cr	/cr/	as in crab
dr	/dr/	as in drum
tr	/tr/	as in tree
fl	/fl/	as in flag
fr	/fr/	as in frog
gl	/gl/	as in glasses
gr	/gr/	as in grass
pl	/pl/	as in plate
pr	/pr/	as in pram
sc	/sc/	as in scarf
sk	/sk/	as in skate
sm	/sm/	as in smile
sn	/sn/	as in snake
sl	/sl/	as in sleep
sp	/sp/	as in spider
st	/st/	as in stop
sw	/sw/	as in sweet
lt	/lt/	as in belt
mp	/mp/	as in stamp
nd	/nd/	as in hand
nt	/nt/	as in plant
st	/st/	as in nest

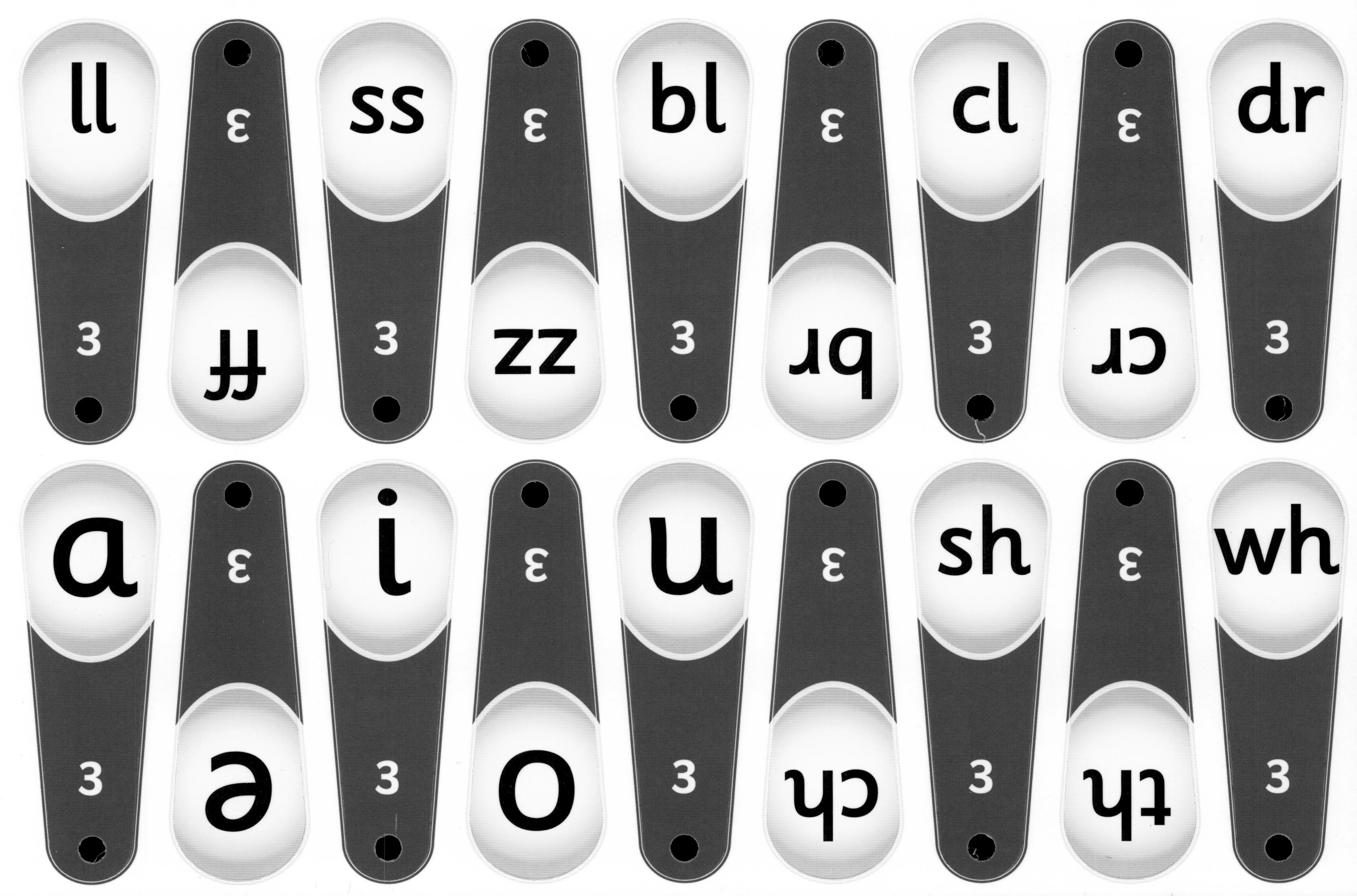
ll
ss
bl
cl
dr
a
i
u
sh
wh
ff
zz
br
cr
e
o
ch
th

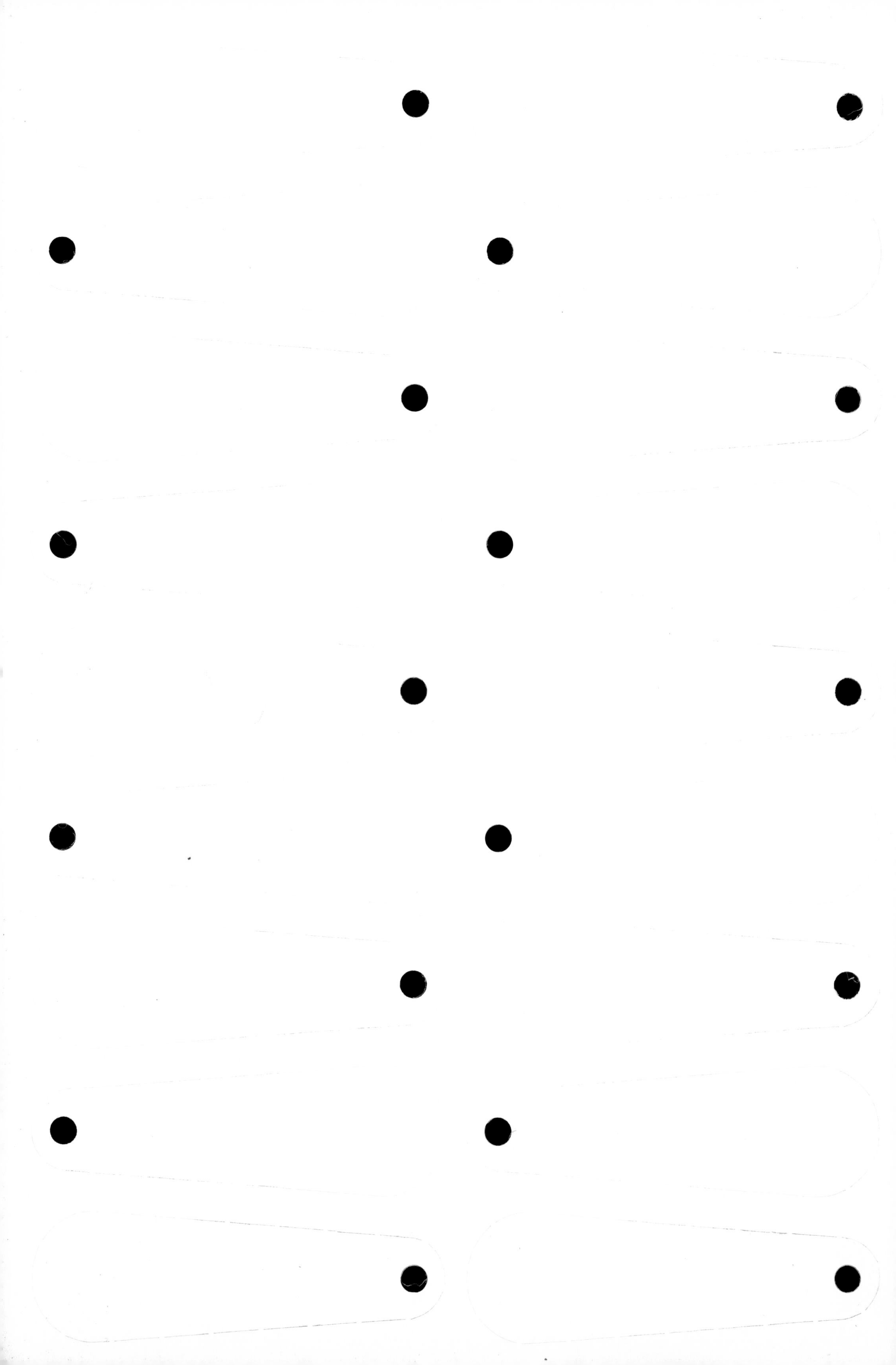

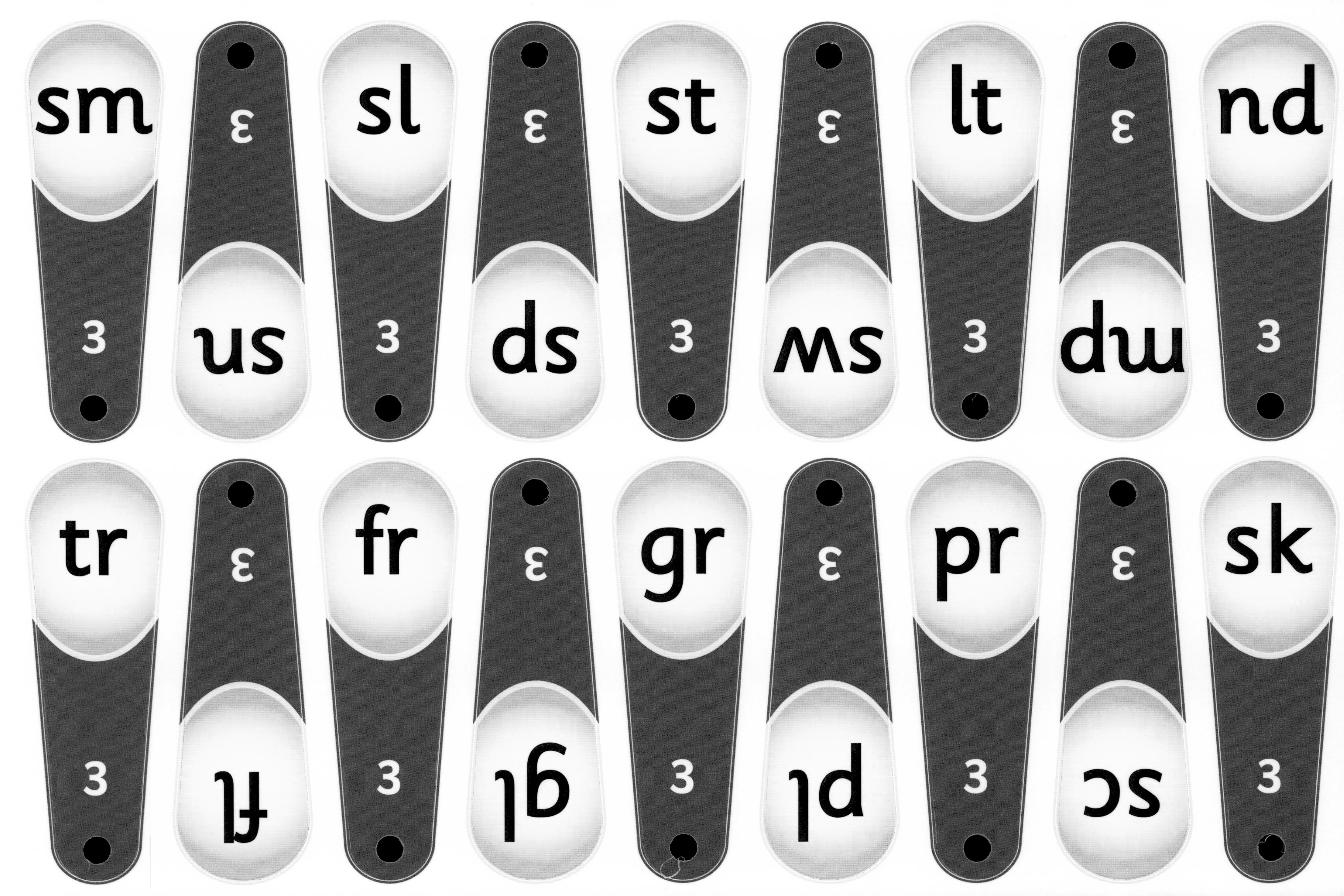
sm
sn
sl
sp
st
sw
lt
mp
nd
tr
fl
fr
gl
gr
pl
pr
sc
sk

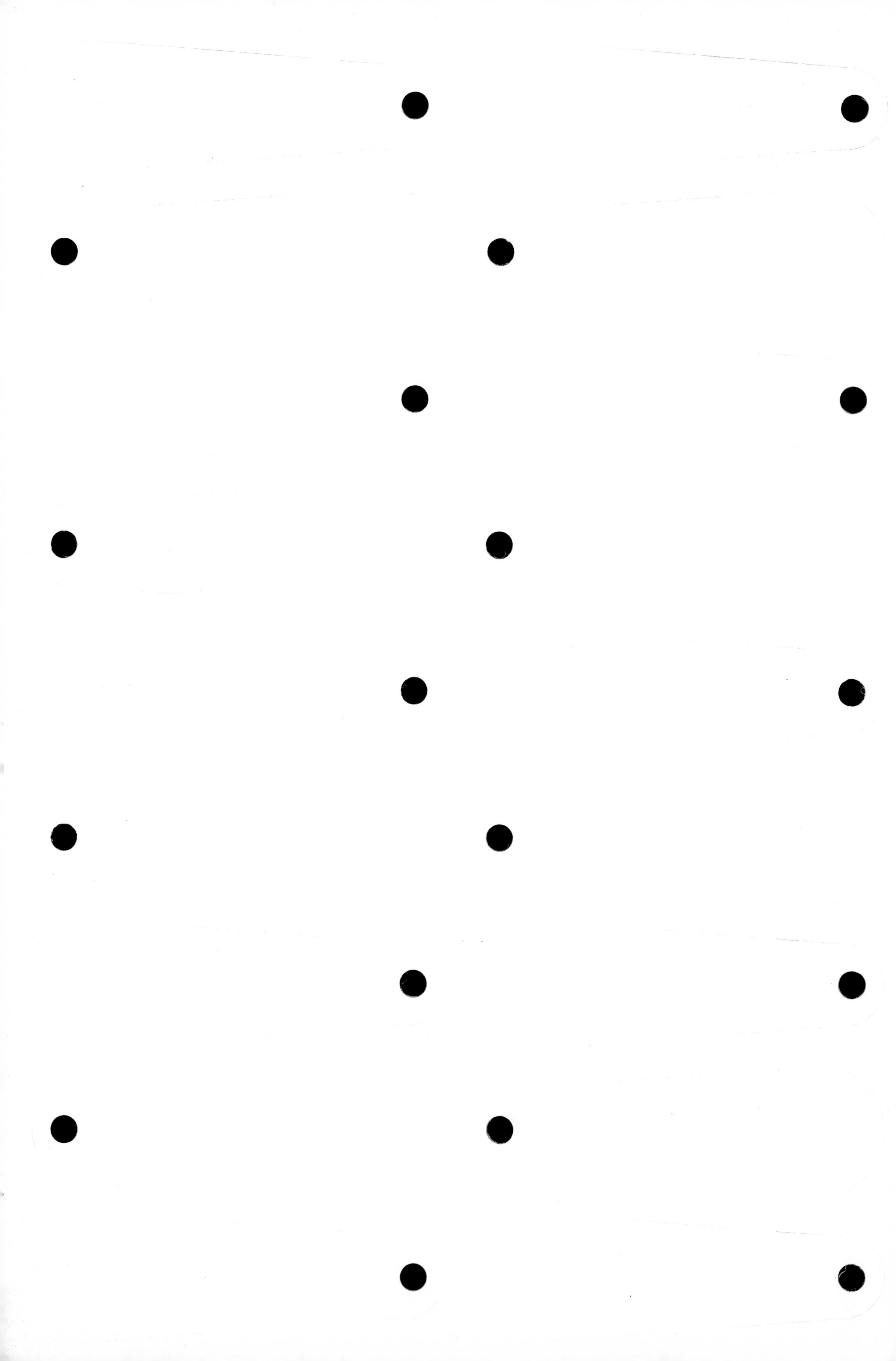

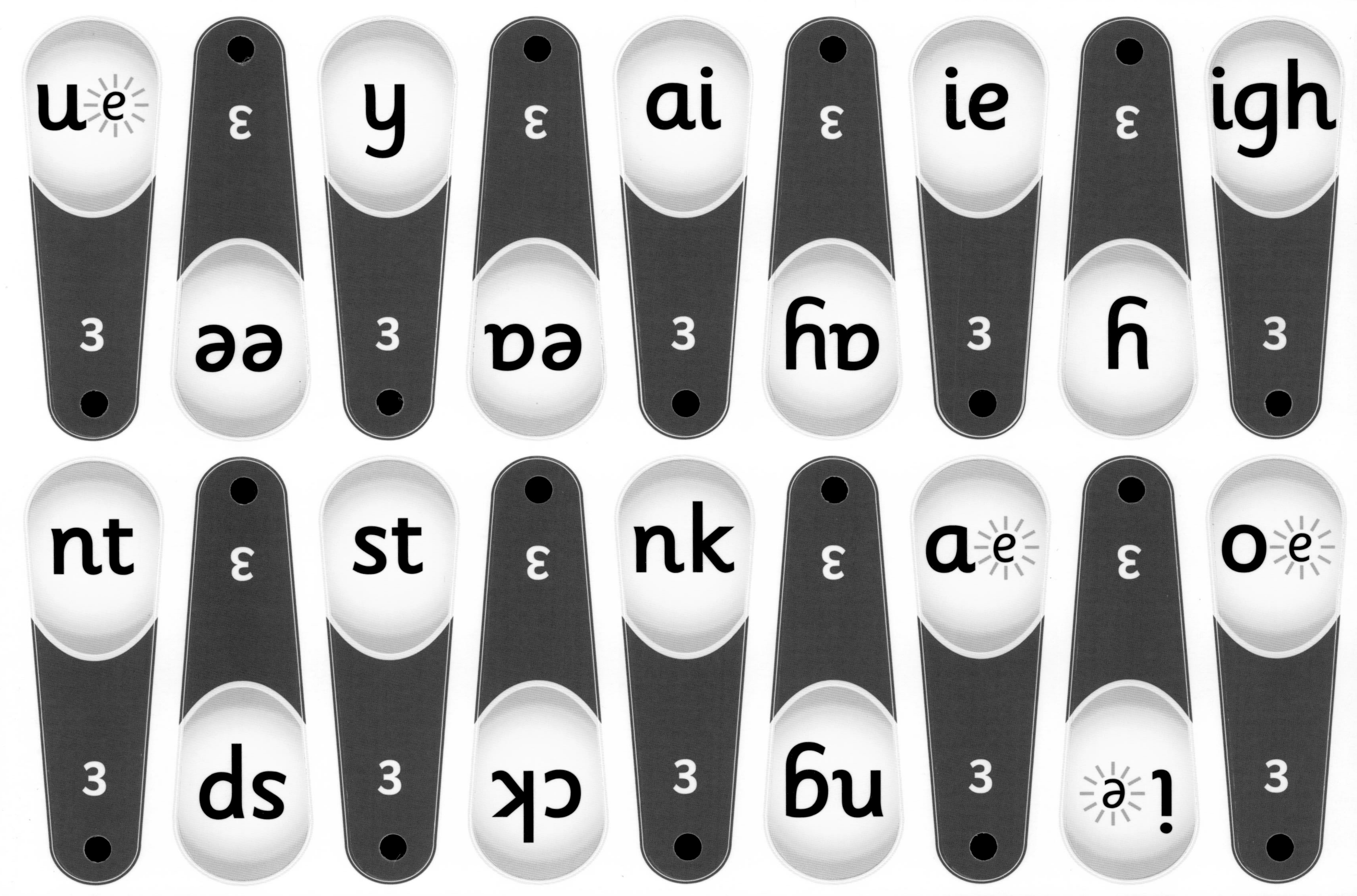

u-e
y
ai
ie
igh
ee
ea
ay
y
nt
st
nk
a-e
o-e
sp
ck
ng
i-e
3

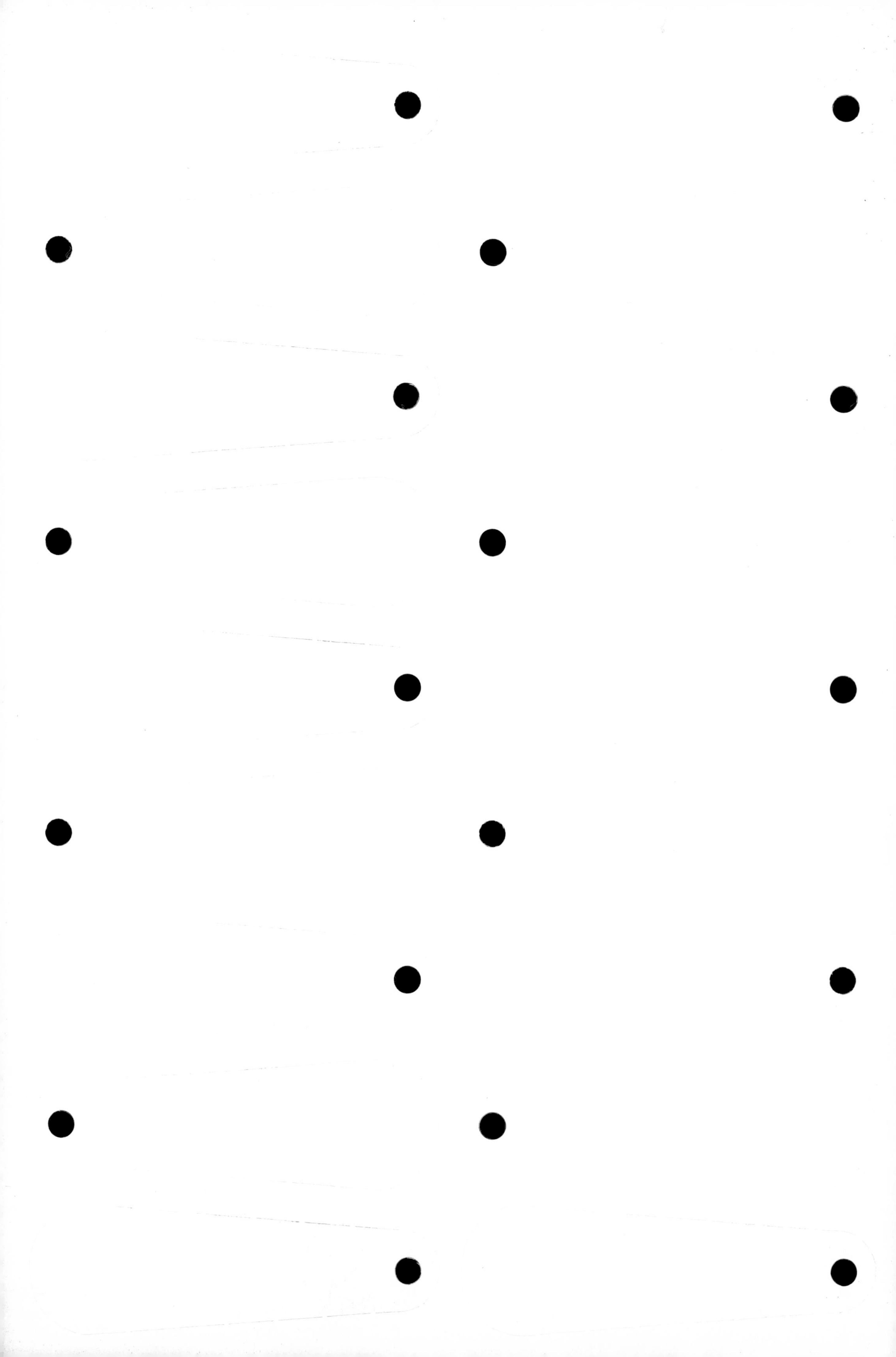

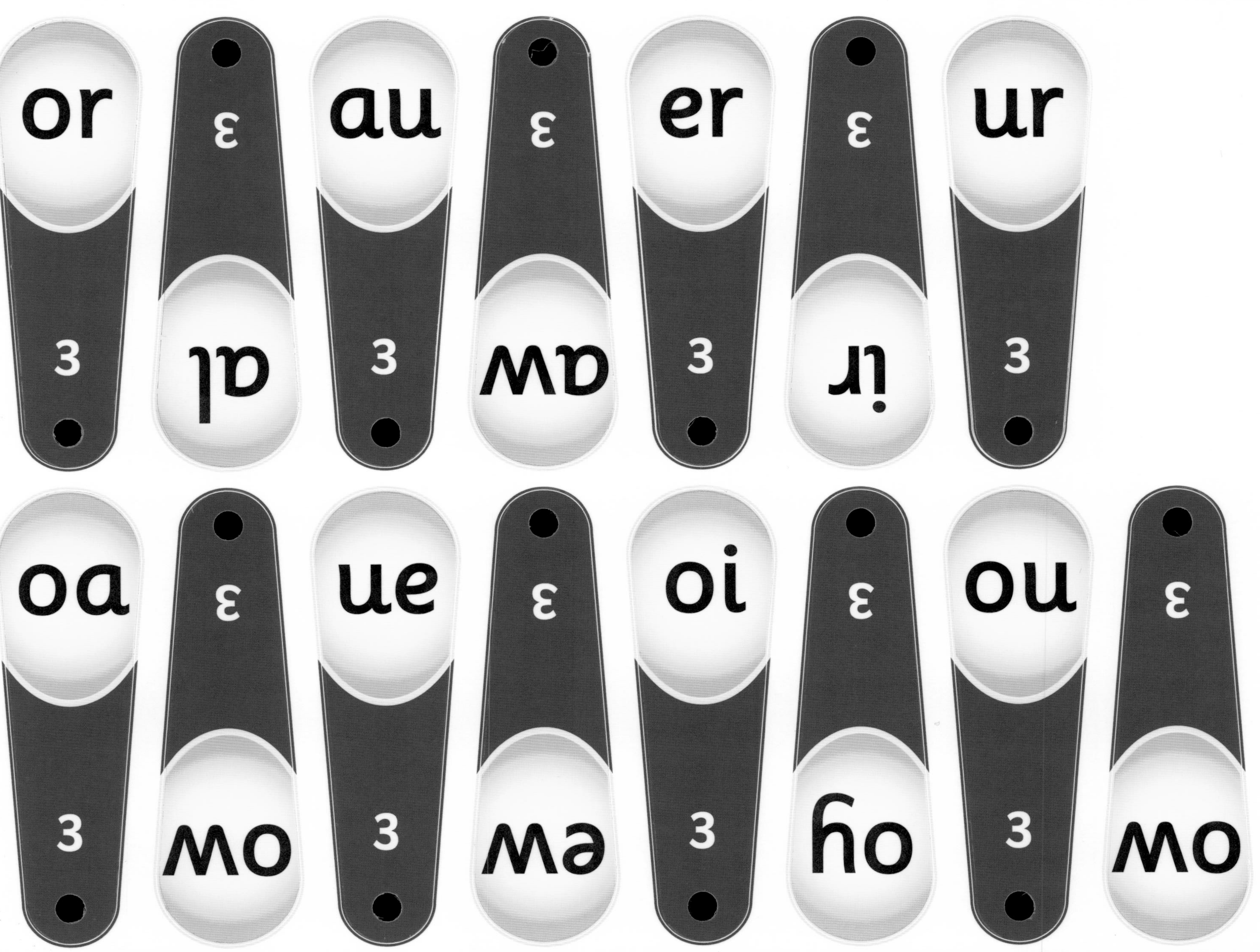
or
al
au
aw
er
ir
ur
oa
ow
ue
ew
oi
oy
ou
ow

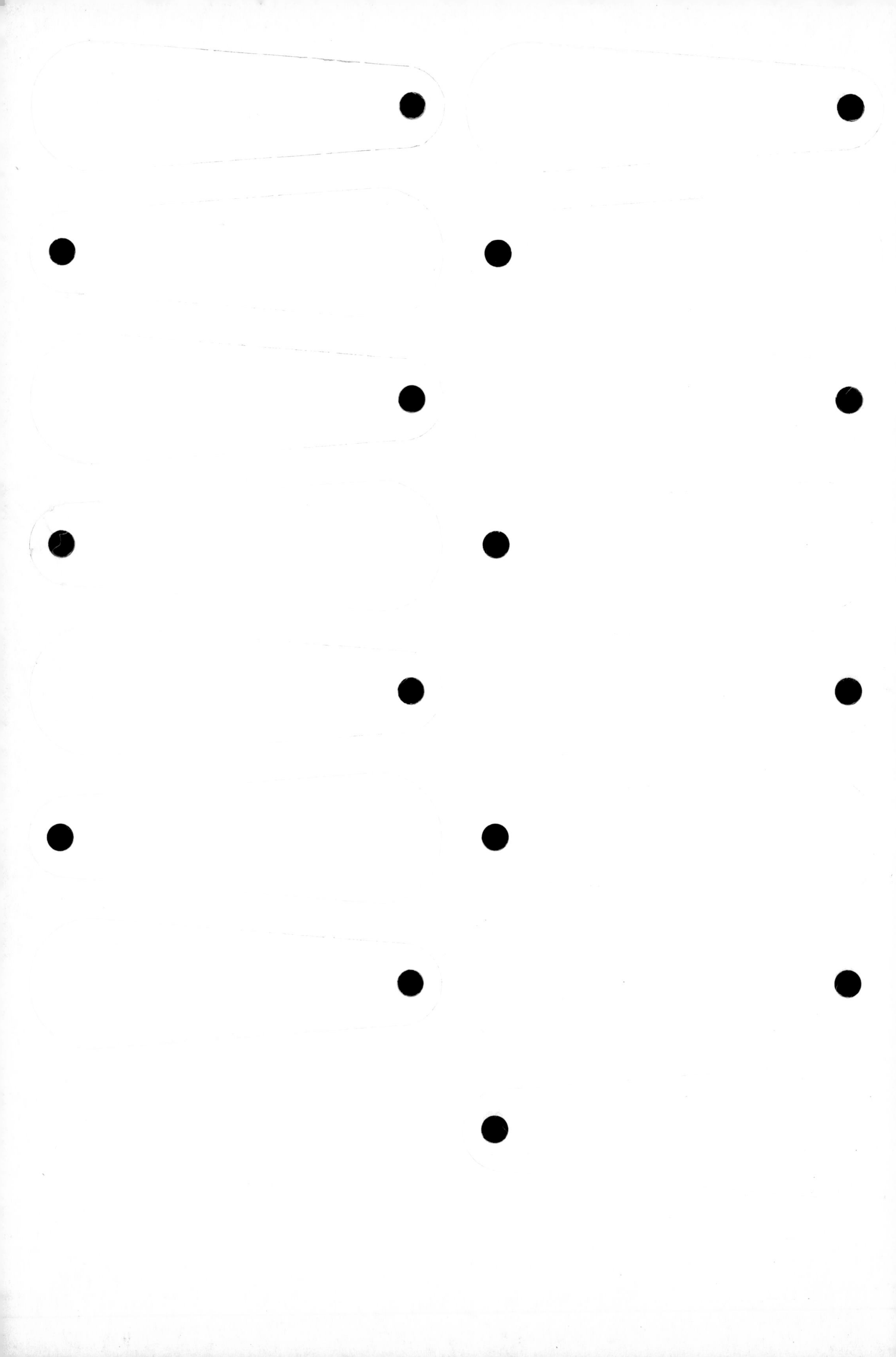